LOGIC: *The Theory of Formal Inference*

51222

Alice Ambrose

Morris Lazerowitz

Smith College

Logic:

THE THEORY OF

FORMAL INFERENCE

160
A496

HOLT, RINEHART AND WINSTON

New York

Contents

LOGIC: *The Theory of Formal Inference*

[I]

Truth-functions

Introduction

The term "logic", understood as designating the general theory of exact reasoning, has traditionally been used as a covering term for quite different subject matters: inductive, or probable, inference, and a special kind of deductive inference. Aristotle (385–322 B.C.), the great Greek philosopher, was the first to investigate inferences of the latter kind, inferences in which, to employ his description, "certain things being stated, something other than what is stated follows of necessity from their being so". The theory Aristotle developed extended to, but not beyond, the requirements of immediate inference and the syllogism, i.e., it covered deductive inferences made from single statements and inferences drawn from pairs of statements of certain kinds. This initial flowering of logic was followed by a dormancy of some two thousand years; and when, about a hundred years ago, logic again sprang to life, it developed enormously in the direction of generality and system, with the result that syllogistic doctrine came to occupy only a minor place in it. In its latest developments logic was seen to be linked to mathematics, and even thought to be the foundation on which the system of mathematics rests. Thus the science which first began with what Aristotle called "Analytics" (some hundreds of years later given the designation "logic" by Alexander of Aphrodisias) has now undergone a development which ranks it as a mathematical discipline.

In this introduction to logic we shall confine ourselves to what is called *formal* logic, as distinct from that branch of the subject which investigates probable inference. And we shall begin, quite unhistorically, with the most general part of logic and move on to more specific parts, within which the syllogism finds a much humbler place than with the ancients. We turn immediately to a description of the kind of deductive inferences that formal logic investigates. Aristotle's description of deductive inferences, intended only to cover that restricted class which he investigated, is even too wide for the whole class of inferences with which logic deals. Inferences in which, according to Aristotle, "something . . . follows of necessity", constitute all possible deductive inferences, whereas

1

the deductive inferences which are the subject matter of formal logic are only a subclass of these. To illustrate the distinction between non-formal and formal deductive inferences, consider, as an instance of the former, the deduction of "*a* has 12 edges" from "*a* is a cube". Given that *a* is a cube it follows of necessity that *a* has 12 edges. To assent to the given necessitates admission of the consequence; one cannot consistently admit the premise while denying that *a* has 12 edges. This inference, which is effected by means of the pair of concepts, *cube* and *having 12 edges*, stands in sharp contrast to the inference from the premise

to the conclusion   If *a* is a cube, *a* has 12 edges
                       If *a* does not have 12 edges, *a* is not a cube.

The difference may be made perspicuous by replacing the concepts *cube* and *having 12 edges* by pairs of brackets in each inference:

Premise: *a* is (   ), Conclusion: *a* is [   ];
Premise: If *a* is (   ), then *a* is [   ], Conclusion: If *a* is not [   ], then *a* is not (   ).

The first inference is effected solely in virtue of the particular concepts *cube* and *having 12 edges*. It would, obviously, not hold for every pair of concepts. For example, given that *a* is blue we are not entitled to infer that *a* is square. But the second inference holds for all possible pairs of concepts, regardless even of whether the statements in which they figure are relevant to each other. Thus, from the statement, "If it is snowing in Alaska, butter is a medium of exchange in Tibet", we may validly infer the statement, "If butter is not a medium of exchange in Tibet, it is not snowing in Alaska". The transition from one statement to the other is effected in virtue of their formal relations to each other. We pause to remark the even more striking difference between all these deductive inferences and the inference from "Sirens are sounding" to "There is fire". In this inference the premise does no more than lend a degree of probability to the conclusion and does not necessitate it; the assertion of the premise together with the denial of the conclusion is a *possible* truth.

    In logic methods are devised for calculating new statements from given statements solely by reference to their forms, or, to put it differently, techniques are invented for testing the validity of formal inferences. To explain this description of logic, it is required to distinguish between the *form* of a statement and its *material content*. The notion of form in abstraction from content is intuitively grasped when one sees what is common to "*If* the figure is a cube, *then* it has 12 edges" and "*If* Jones is a Mexican, *then* he is soft-spoken". Once the subject matter of the two statements is disregarded, what is left is a bare schema exhibiting how the constituent statements are related. Provisionally we may say that the form of a statement is what remains when the constituents have been replaced by variables, the same constituents by the same variables and different constituents by different variables. The role of blanks enclosed by pairs of brackets in the expressions above is that of variables. The resultant expressions are said to consist solely of formal terms, the variables themselves counting as formal terms.

Formal Terms

The units figuring in inferences are statements, which are characterized by the property of being either true or false, or of having a *truth-value*. By virtue of the formal terms occurring in statements, logic provides a means of calculating the truth-value of a statement from that of the given statement. The expression "formal term" is defined here *ostensively*, that is, by giving a list of terms to which it applies. We introduce as our first formal terms variables "p", "q", "r", ..., whose range of values consists of statements. Next introduced are two formal terms of a different kind: "or", for which the symbol "$\vee$" is used, and "not", for which the symbol "$\sim$" is used. These will be classed together as *operators* and assigned special names: "$\vee$" will be called *disjunction* and "$\sim$" will be called *negation*. The expression

$$\sim p$$

is read "p is false" or, alternatively, "not-p". A statement of the form "$\sim p$" will be true if "p" is false, and false if "p" is true; and "$\sim(\sim p)$", the negation of "$\sim p$", amounts simply to "p". It is obvious that "$\sim$" can operate on a statement no part of which is a statement, whereas "$\vee$" requires at least two statements for its operation. Both terms can of course operate on statements which are themselves made up of statements.

In ordinary English "or" is used to mean "one or the other". In some instances of its use it is understood to present mutually exclusive alternatives, while in other instances the condition of exclusiveness is understood not to hold, i.e., it sometimes means "one or the other but not both" and sometimes "one or the other or both". In logic convenience dictates its use in the nonexclusive sense, to mean that at least one of the stated alternatives is the case. Thus,

$$p \vee q$$

may be read "at least one, p, q, is true", and taken as neither specifying which of the two is true nor whether both are true. It is to be noted that "$\vee$" has some of the properties of the arithmetic operators "$+$" and "$\times$": it is *commutative*, that is, the order of the disjuncts "p" and "q" is immaterial, so that there is no need to distinguish between "$p \vee q$" and "$q \vee p$". It is *associative*, that is, "$p \vee (q \vee r)$" and "$(p \vee q) \vee r$" both amount simply to "$p \lor q \lor r$", since internal grouping is immaterial, just as it is in "$x + y + z$" and "$x \times y \times z$". In one important respect "$\lor$" differs from either "$+$" or "$\times$", namely, in that "$p \lor p$" comes to the same thing as "p", whereas "$x + x$" and "$x \times x$" are not identical with "x".

In addition to variables and operators some means of punctuation is required for the expression of logical form. For this purpose we shall use either dots or brackets or a combination of the two. We shall start with brackets and shall introduce the dot form of punctuation when convenience requires it. The list of formal terms now consists of

Statement variables:	$p, q, r, \ldots$
Negation:	$\sim$
Disjunction:	$\lor$
Punctuation:	$(\,,); [\,,];$ etc.

It is to be remarked that although statement variables are the only variables as yet at our disposal, they are not the only ones used in logic. Variables which replace parts of statements that are not themselves statements will be introduced later, and the addition of these to the list will enable us to formulate rules of inference which cannot be formulated in terms of the present logical material. Part I will be confined to the apparatus set out above. This is to say that the part of logic to be developed first is the so-called theory of *truth-functions*. The name "truth-function" is given to those statement-forms (1) which result from suppressing all parts of statements which are not formal terms, (2) the variables of which have statements exclusively as their values.

By means of the formal terms now at hand it is possible to give the logical forms of many statements, for example,

$$p \lor \sim q, \quad \sim(\sim p \lor q), \quad \sim p \lor q \lor r, \quad \sim p \lor \sim[q \lor (\sim r \lor s)].$$

The statements

> Either he studies or he does not pass the exam

and

> It is not the case that either it does not rain in East Africa or it pours

have, respectively, "$p \lor \sim q$" and "$\sim(\sim p \lor q)$" as their forms. The reader can find statements of which the remainder are forms. It will be noted how much more perspicuously the notation used here exhibits logical form than does ordinary English. To use the last expression as an illustration, the English reading is:

> Either "p" is false, or else it is false that either "q" is true or "not-r or s" is true.

Disjunctive Arguments

On exhibiting the logical structure of statements in the compact statement-forms the newly introduced symbolism permits, it becomes a simple matter to calculate the truth-values of statements from given statements by reference exclusively to their forms. For example, given that a statement of the form "$p \lor q$" is true and also that "$\sim q$" is true, we are entitled to infer that "p" is true. The inference of "p" from "$p \lor q$" together with "$\sim q$" is a calculation, such as Leibniz (1646–1716) envisioned for inclusion in his "calculus ratiocinatur". This inference-calculation, and others similar to it, may be represented by arranging premises and conclusion as follows:

$$(1) \quad \frac{p \lor q}{p} \quad \sim q \; .$$

To illustrate: Suppose a detective has discovered that either Jones or Smith is implicated in a certain fraud, and finally determines that Smith is not implicated. He can correctly infer that Jones *is* implicated. On the other hand, given "$p \lor q$" and "q", he is justified in inferring nothing as to the truth-value of "p". For since the fact that at least one of the men is implicated in the fraud does not exclude their both being implicated, the discovery that Smith is implicated allows no inference as to whether Jones is or is not implicated. This shows up clearly in the schema

$$(2) \quad \frac{p \lor q}{?} \quad q$$

Elaborations on schemata (1) and (2) may be multiplied. For example, given as true that one of three scientific hypotheses explains a phenomenon, and also that one of them is false, it can be inferred that either one of the other two hypotheses is true:

$$(1a) \quad \frac{p \lor q \lor r}{p \lor r} \quad \sim q$$

If, however, we are given "$p \lor q \lor r$", "$\sim q$", and also "r", nothing with regard to the truth-value of "p" can be inferred:

$$(2a) \quad \frac{p \lor q \lor r}{?} \quad \sim q, r$$

Again, if the truth-value of "$p \vee q$" is initially unknown, then given that "q" is true we may validly infer "$p \vee q$", and given "$\sim q$" we may infer "$p \vee \sim q$":

$$\text{(3)} \quad \frac{q}{p \vee q}\,, \qquad \text{(3a)} \quad \frac{\sim q}{p \vee \sim q}\,.$$

But from "$\sim q$", "$p \vee q$" is not formally inferrible:

$$\text{(4)} \quad \frac{\sim q}{?}\,.$$

Conjunction

Let us turn to the following more complex form of inference:

$$\text{(5)} \quad \frac{\sim[\sim(p \vee q) \vee \sim(r \vee q)]}{\sim p \vee \sim r} \\ \overline{} \\ q$$

For a concrete instance of this logical schema make the following replace-ments: for "p", "I speak the truth", for "q", "I suffer", for "r", "I lie". The first premise then reads: "It is not the case either that it is false that I speak the truth or suffer, or false that I lie or suffer".

The formulation of this inference-schema is more complicated than it need be, and it can be re-expressed more simply, with a consequent economy of reasoning, by introducing a further formal term. This is the familiar "and", which is symbolized by "." and called *conjunction*. The expression

$$p \cdot q,$$

read "p and q", is to the effect that "p" and "q" are jointly true. Like "$p \vee q$", "$p \cdot q$" is commutative and associative, and "$p \cdot p$" comes to the same thing as "p". By contrast with "$p \vee q$", which is true when either disjunct is true and false only when both disjuncts are false, "$p \cdot q$" is false if either conjunct is false, and true only when both conjuncts are true.* Despite this difference in the two operators, what makes it possible to simplify the complex form of inference (5) is the fact that "$p \cdot q$" is completely definable in terms of "$\vee$" and "$\sim$". This fact implies that the introduction of the new term actually adds no material over and above what we already have in the list of formal terms. What can be said by means of "." can be said by means of "$\vee$" and "$\sim$". Thus if we begin, as

---

* We speak of "$p \vee q$" and "$p \cdot q$" being true, which is improper, as these are not statements. The expressions " '$p \vee q$' is true", " '$p \cdot q$' is true" are to be understood as being short for "a statement of the form $p \vee q$ ($p \cdot q$) is true".

we have begun, with "v" and "∼", the symbol "." may be introduced by definition:

$$p \cdot q = \text{Df.} \sim (\sim p \vee \sim q).$$

To say it is false that either "p" is false or "q" is false obviously comes to the same thing as saying that both "p" and "q" are true: "neither not-p nor not-q" amounts to "both p and q".

If we had begun with "." and "∼", the symbol "v" might in analogous fashion have been introduced by definition:

$$p \vee q = \text{Df.} \sim (\sim p \cdot \sim q).$$

To say it is false that both "p" and "q" are false is the same as to say that at least one, "p", "q", is true. The expressions on either side of the symbol "= Df.", which ushers in the definition, may replace each other as desired. Thus, the statement "Both 3 and 5 are odd" is interchangeable with the statement "It is false that either 3 is not odd or 5 is not odd"; and "Either Jones is reading or he is writing" with "It is false that Jones is both not reading and not writing". The simplification in our inference-schema (5) above, made possible by the introduction of ".", is now obvious. The first line of (5), "$\sim[\sim(p \vee q) \vee \sim(r \vee q)]$", can now be replaced by "$(p \vee q) \cdot (r \vee q)$", analogously to the replacement of "$\sim(\sim p \vee \sim q)$" by "$p \cdot q$". The inference-form (5) becomes

$$\frac{(p \vee q) \cdot (r \vee q)}{\sim p \vee \sim r} \quad ,$$
$$q$$

and is easily seen to be valid.

The possibility of replacing the conjunction "$p \cdot q$" by the negation of a disjunction, and the disjunction "$p \vee q$" by the negation of a conjunction, suggests a general rule for transforming other conjunctions and disjunctions, for example,

$$p \cdot \sim q, \qquad\qquad \sim p \vee \sim q$$

into $\qquad\qquad$ into

$$\sim(\sim p \vee q) \qquad\qquad \sim(p \cdot q).$$

Conversely, it suggests a rule for expressing the result of the operation negation upon a disjunction or conjunction. Calling the statement-forms connected within the brackets by "v" or "." the *arguments*, we can formulate the two rules* in the following way:

(A) the negation of a disjunction is the conjunction of the negated arguments;

(B) the negation of a conjunction is the disjunction of the negated arguments.

* After the rules formulated for analogous class-formulas by Augustus De Morgan (1806–1871).

It is of some interest to see how the pieces of formal reasoning (1) through (5) can be restated in terms of "$\sim$" and ".", with entire neglect of "v":

(1') $\sim(\sim p \,.\, \sim q)$
$$\frac{\sim q}{p},$$

(2') $\sim(\sim p \,.\, \sim q)$
$$\frac{q}{?},$$

(1a') $\sim(\sim p \,.\, \sim q \,.\, \sim r)$
$$\frac{\sim q}{\sim(\sim p \,.\, \sim r)},$$

(2a') $\sim(\sim p \,.\, \sim q \,.\, \sim r)$
$$\frac{\sim q \,.\, r}{?},$$

(3') $$\frac{q}{\sim(\sim p \,.\, \sim q)},$$

(3a') $$\frac{\sim q}{\sim(\sim p \,.\, q)},$$

(4') $$\frac{\sim q}{?},$$

(5') $\sim(\sim p \,.\, \sim q) \,.\, \sim(\sim r \,.\, \sim q)$
$$\frac{\sim(p \,.\, r)}{q}.$$

Implication and Equivalence

It is convenient and psychologically simpler to use both terms, "." and "v", than to confine ourselves to only one of these, as is obvious on comparing the various formulations of (5). In fact, the same sort of consideration dictates the introduction of two further terms, each definable by means of "v" and "$\sim$", and of course alternatively by "." and "$\sim$". These are "if ... then ----", or "implies", symbolized by "$\supset$", and "equivalence", symbolized by "$\equiv$". The expression "$p \supset q$", in which "p" is called the *antecedent* and "q" the *consequent*, is defined

$$p \supset q = \text{Df. } \sim p \text{ v } q.$$

We justify the definition by means of an example. Consider the implicative statements, expressed in the form "If p then q",

> If buying power diminishes, a depression is likely
> If the switch is depressed, the light will come on.

These say precisely what is said by

> Either buying power does not diminish or a depression is likely
> Either the switch is not depressed or the light will come on.

The definition of "equivalence" is most naturally expressed by means of the defined terms "$\supset$" and ".":

$$p \equiv q = \text{Df. } (p \supset q) \,.\, (q \supset p).$$

For example, that "a is an even prime" is equivalent to "$a = 2$" is the same as the fact that "a is an even prime" both implies and is implied by "$a = 2$": if a is an even prime, $a = 2$, and if $a = 2$, a is an even prime. The symbol "$\equiv$" could, as might be expected, be defined in terms of "$\sim$" and "v", in terms of "$\sim$" and ".", or in terms of "$\sim$" and "$\supset$". It is of some interest to see what the defining expression in each case is:

$$\sim[\sim(\sim p \vee q) \vee \sim(\sim q \vee p)]$$
$$\sim(p . \sim q) . \sim(q . \sim p)$$
$$\sim[(p \supset q) \supset \sim(q \supset p)].$$

When two statements are equivalent, or mutually imply each other, either is said to be both a *necessary* and *sufficient* condition for the other. Any statement "p" is a sufficient condition for "q" when "$p \supset q$". And it is a necessary condition when "$\sim p \supset \sim q$", or, what comes to the same thing, when "$q \supset p$". (For "$q \supset p$" becomes "$\sim q \vee p$", which can be seen to be "$\sim p \supset \sim q$".) To return to the example above, a's being an even prime is a sufficient condition for the truth of "$a = 2$". It is also a necessary condition: Only if a is an even prime is $a = 2$, so that if a is not an even prime "$a = 2$" must be false. In general, the sufficient and necessary conditions for the truth of a statement "q" are not the same. For example, "a is equilateral" is sufficient for the truth of "a is isosceles", but not necessary; whereas "a is an even number between 2 and 7" is necessary but not sufficient for the truth of "$a = 4$". Only when there is an equivalence between "p" and "q" do both conditions hold. It will be recognized that transformations of formulas by means of the negation rules given above produce equivalents.

Negation of Mixed Functions

It is useful at this point to note that the rules for negating disjunctions and for negating conjunctions may be extended to cover functions involving mixtures of the two operators, e.g.,

$$\sim[p \vee \sim(q . r . s)] \equiv (\sim p . q . r . s),$$

and also to functions involving other operators as well. By transforming a negated expression into one involving only ".", "v", and "$\sim$" we obtain an expression to which the original rules apply:

$$\sim\{p \supset [q \equiv (r . s)]\} \equiv \sim\{\sim p \vee [(\sim q \vee (r . s)) . (\sim(r . s) \vee q)]\}$$
$$\equiv p . \sim[(\sim q \vee (r . s)) . (\sim(r . s) \vee q)]$$
$$\equiv p . [\sim(\sim q \vee (r . s)) \vee \sim(\sim(r . s) \vee q)]$$
$$\equiv p . [(q . (\sim r \vee \sim s)) \vee (r . s . \sim q)]$$

Properties of Implication

The pieces of reasoning on formal terms, (1) through (5), are standard-ized forms which can be summed up into prescriptions for, or rules of, inference. Thus, (1) may be summed up in the rule, *denying one argument of a disjunction necessitates affirming the remaining argument*; (2) can be summed up in the rule, *affirming one argument allows no inference to the other*. Comparable rules can be formulated for implication. On the basis of the following two inference-schemata

$$\textbf{(6)} \quad \frac{\begin{array}{c} p \supset q \\ p \end{array}}{q} \, , \qquad \textbf{(7)} \quad \frac{\begin{array}{c} p \supset q \\ \sim q \end{array}}{\sim p} \, ,$$

we can formulate the rules of *affirming the antecedent* and of *denying the consequent*, respectively: *affirming the antecedent of an implication necessi-tates affirming the consequent, denying the consequent of an implication necessitates denying the antecedent*. That the above forms of reasoning are justified appears immediately on transforming "$p \supset q$" into "$\sim p \vee q$", whereupon both reduce to cases of denying a disjunct. The fallacious forms of reasoning,

$$\frac{\begin{array}{c} p \supset q \\ \sim p \end{array}}{\sim q} \, , \qquad \frac{\begin{array}{c} p \supset q \\ q \end{array}}{p} \, ,$$

correspond to inferences from disjunctions in which the second premise affirms one disjunct. Each form of argument confuses a sufficient condi-tion for the truth of "q" with a necessary one: In each case "p" is illicitly taken to be the only condition for "q"'s truth. Or to put it otherwise, "$p \supset q$" is identified with "$q \supset p$". Transformation of these functions into disjunctions together with an examination of the conditions that make each false and that make each true will show that not all these conditions are the same, as would be required if "$p \supset q$" and "$q \supset p$" were equivalent. This test will show that, by contrast, "$p \supset q$" and "$\sim q \supset \sim p$", "$q \supset p$" and "$\sim p \supset \sim q$", do come to the same thing; and this means that each can be validly inferred from the other. Other forms of valid inference, resting on the so-called *transitivity* property of implica-tion, are

$$\textbf{(8)} \quad \frac{\begin{array}{c} p \supset q \\ q \supset r \end{array}}{p \supset r} \, , \qquad \textbf{(9)} \quad \frac{\begin{array}{c} p \supset q \\ \sim r \supset \sim q \end{array}}{\sim r \supset \sim p} \, .$$

In (8) the consequent of one premise is the antecedent of the other; and the same is true of (9) when one of the premises is replaced by its impli-cational equivalent.

In cases where the truth-value of "$p \supset q$" is unknown, it is interesting to note which conditions allow us to calculate its truth-values:

$$\frac{q}{p \supset q}, \quad \frac{\sim p}{p \supset q}, \quad \frac{\sim p \cdot q}{p \supset q}, \quad \frac{p \cdot \sim q}{\sim(p \supset q)}.$$

It may seem odd that an "if . . . then - - -" statement should be true under the conditions (1) that its consequent is true and (2) that its antecedent is false. That "$p \supset q$" is true under these conditions is made evident by transforming it into "$\sim p \lor q$", as is also the fact that "$p \supset q$" is false under the single condition "$p \cdot \sim q$". An extension of the first two calculations above can be made to "chain" implications such as "$p \supset [q \supset (r \supset s)]$" in which the sign of implication in each case governs the expression succeeding it. Suppose the truth-value of "$p \supset [q \supset (r \supset s)]$" is unknown. Given that the final consequent "s" is true, or that any antecedent is false, the truth of the chain implication follows:

$$\frac{s}{p \supset [q \supset (r \supset s)]}, \quad \frac{\sim p}{p \supset [q \supset (r \supset s)]},$$

$$\frac{\sim q}{p \supset [q \supset (r \supset s)]}, \quad \frac{\sim r}{p \supset [q \supset (r \supset s)]}.$$

Applications

Problems which, without the apparatus developed so far, would present considerable difficulties can now be dealt with simply. Consider the following, of which the schema appears alongside:

(1) It is the case both that if I drink coffee, then if I count sheep, I do not fall asleep, and also that if I do not drink coffee I am not nervous

$$[p \supset (q \supset \sim r)] \cdot (\sim p \supset \sim s)$$

(2) I am nervous s

(3) I count sheep q

Do I fall asleep?   ?

The conjunction of "s" with "$\sim p \supset \sim s$" yields "p", by the rule of denying the consequent, and "p" together with "$p \supset (q \supset \sim r)$" yields "$q \supset \sim r$", by the rule of affirming the antecedent. From "$q \supset \sim r$" conjoined with "q" we derive the answer to the question, namely, that I do not fall asleep.

$$\frac{\sim p \supset \sim s \quad s}{p}, \quad \frac{p \supset (q \supset \sim r) \quad p}{q \supset \sim r}, \quad \frac{q \supset \sim r \quad q}{\sim r}.$$

Consider the following, more complicated, problem.

(1) If either it is false that Jones did not witness the collision or Smith was wearing his spectacles when he saw the collision, then if Coe was the driver of the stolen truck, then if the third witness was not intimidated, the judge was bribed
(2) If the third witness was not intimidated, Coe was the driver of the stolen truck
(3) The judge was not bribed
(4) The third witness was not intimidated

Was Smith wearing his spectacles when he saw the collision?

The schema for these premises is:

(1) $(\sim\sim p \vee q) \supset [r \supset (\sim s \supset u)]$
(2) $\sim s \supset r$
(3) $\sim u$
(4) $\sim s.$

The conjunction of (2) and (4) yields "r", and the conjunction of (3) and (4) falsifies the consequent of "$r \supset (\sim s \supset u)$". Hence the conjunction of (2), (3), and (4) falsifies the consequent of (1), inasmuch as it falsifies the disjunction "$\sim r \vee s \vee u$". Thus the falsity of the antecedent of (1), namely, "$\sim(\sim\sim p \vee q)$", or "$\sim p . \sim q$", can be inferred. From this it follows that Smith was not wearing his spectacles when he saw the collision.

$$\frac{\sim s \supset r \quad \sim s}{r} \; , \quad \frac{r . \sim s . \sim u}{\sim[r \supset (\sim s \supset u)]} \; ,$$

$$\frac{(\sim\sim p \vee q) \supset [r \supset (\sim s \supset u)] \quad \sim[r \supset (\sim s \supset u)]}{\sim(\sim\sim p \vee q)} \; , \quad \frac{\sim p . \sim q}{\sim q} \; .$$

Formal Validity and Tautologous Functions

The problem of devising methods for calculating formally the consequences of given statements is the same as that of devising methods for determining whether a formal inference is *valid*. That is, calculating a consequence B from a premise A is the same as determining that A $\supset$ B is formally valid, or that B does follow from A in virtue of their formal properties. Some functions of the form A $\supset$ B are such that no matter what statements are substituted for the component statement variables of A and B, the result is a true statement. This is also the case with other truth-functions constructed solely from the logical materials so far announced, i.e., from statement variables and other operators than "⊃". Such forms are called *tautologies*. An obvious example is

$$(p . \sim q) \supset (p . \sim q).$$

No matter what statements are substituted for "p" and "q", the result will be a statement which is true, and furthermore, true in virtue of its form. Another obvious tautology is "$p \vee \sim p$". Somewhat more complicated tautologies are

$$(p \supset q) \supset (\sim q \supset \sim p), \qquad (p . q) \supset (p \vee q), \qquad (\sim p . q) \supset q.$$

If in each of the two preceding problems the given and the derived answer are connected as antecedent and consequent, a still more complex tautology results:

$$[(1) . (2) . (3)] \supset \sim r, \qquad [(1) . (2) . (3) . (4)] \supset \sim q.$$

Truth-tables

The problem of determining whether B follows formally from A now reduces to the problem of devising a method for determining whether A ⊃ B is a tautology. For this purpose the so-called *matrix method* or *method of truth-tables* has been invented. This method is a schematic device for correlating the truth-values of the component statements, called *truth-conditions*, with the truth-value they determine the statement to have. Writing T and F for "true" and "false", the truth-conditions are given in a compact array of combinations of T's and F's together with the correlated truth-values of the statement. These are presented in the form of a table in which the truth-conditions are listed on the left and the correlated truth-values under the statement on the right. Thus the truth-tables for "$\sim p$", "$p \vee q$", "$p . q$", "$p \supset q$", and "$p \equiv q$" are:

p	q	$\sim p,$	$p \vee q,$	$p . q,$	$p \supset q,$	$p \equiv q$
T	T	F	T	T	T	T
T	F		T	F	F	F
F	T	T	T	F	T	F
F	F		F	F	T	T

The truth-conditions for "$\sim p$" are two, which in the above table are repeated. They are the T, F entries under "p": "$\sim p$" is false when "p" is true and true when "p" is false. Inasmuch as the remaining functions involve two variables the truth-values of which are independent of each other, the columns on the left must list these truth-values in all possible combinations. There are four such combinations, each of which is a condition under which the given function is either true or false.

The next two tables call for some comment.

(1)

p	$p \vee \sim p$
T	T
F	T

(2)

p	q	$(p \cdot q) \supset (p \supset q)$		
T	T	T	T	T
T	F	F	T	F
F	T	F	T	T
F	F	F	T	T

The first table shows that "$p \vee \sim p$" is true under all possible conditions: "p is true or p is false" is true when "p" is true and also when it is false. And as T and F exhaust "p"'s possible truth-values, "$p \vee \sim p$" always gives rise to a true statement no matter what replacements are made for "p". The second table shows that the function "$(p \cdot q) \supset (p \supset q)$" also is a tautology. The subcolumns beneath "$p \cdot q$" and "$p \supset q$", the two components of the tautologous formula, exhibit the truth-values of each under the same conditions, and from these, looked on as a subsidiary set of truth-conditions, the column of T's beneath the main implication connecting the constituent functions can be calculated. Inasmuch as the table shows no truth-value combination T for the antecedent "$p \cdot q$" with F for the consequent "$p \supset q$", "$(p \cdot q) \supset (p \supset q)$" always holds, which is to say that "$p \supset q$" is a formally valid consequence of "$p \cdot q$".

On the other hand, "$(p \vee q) \supset q$" is not a tautology. The truth-table for it shows this, and at the same time shows why "q" cannot be calculated from "$p \vee q$":

p	q	$(p \vee q) \supset q$		
T	T	T	T T	
T	F	T	F F	
F	T		T	
F	F		T	

The truth-value of the formula is not truth for all of its truth-conditions. And the fact that both T and F under "q" are associated with T under "$p \vee q$" indicates that "q" can have either of two truth-values when "$p \vee q$" is true. This is to say that "q" *need* not be true, and need not be false, when "$p \vee q$" is true, or that nothing regarding "q"'s truth-value can be calculated from the truth of "$p \vee q$".

A truth-function might have been defined as the kind of formula that has a truth-table, one such that the truth-value of the statements obtained by substitutions on its variables is determined uniquely by the truth-values of the substitution statements. The class of truth-function formulas divides into three subclasses, the class of tautologies, the class of inconsistent functions, and the class of contingent functions. A function is contingent if it is true for some of its truth-conditions and false for others; inconsistent if it is false for all its truth-conditions; tautologous if it is false for none. It will be evident that the negation of a tautology is an inconsistent function, and of an inconsistent function a tautology.   It will be evident also that the negation of a contingent function is a contingent function which is true for those conditions for which the original function is false and false for those for which the original function is true.   The matrix method is a procedure for deciding to which class a truth-function belongs. The reader may gain practice in its use by applying the method to the following: "$q \supset (p \lor q)$", "$q \cdot (\sim p \cdot \sim q)$", "$(p \supset q) \supset (q \supset p)$", "$(p \cdot \sim q) \supset (\sim p \supset q)$", "$p \lor (q \cdot \sim q)$", "$p \cdot (q \supset q)$".

Application of Truth-tables to Problems

The class of tautologous formulas are among those traditionally called *laws of logic*. Laws of logic are statement-forms having universal validity, and any inference which conforms to a law of logic is formally valid. It will be instructive to see how the matrix method can be used to decide whether an inference conforms to a law of logic, and is valid, or fails to conform to a law of logic, and is not valid. It turns out that this method can be used to solve problems like those on pages 11–12. In writing a truth-table it must be kept in mind that the number of truth-value combinations of n variables is 2^n. Note that the truth-conditions for functions constructed on two or more variables can be written in a regular way, the rule for which may be gathered from an inspection of the tables applied to the following problems.

(a) Given: (1) If you are a true animal lover, then if you like mice, you do not like cats.

Can the following be validly inferred?

(2) If you like cats, then if you like mice, you are not a true animal lover
(3) If you do not like mice, then if you are a true animal lover, you do not like cats.

The truth-table which gives the answer to the first question is:

p	q	r	$[p \supset (q \supset \sim r)] \supset [r \supset (q \supset \sim p)]$
T	T	T	T
T	T	F	T
T	F	T	T
T	F	F	T
F	T	T	T
F	T	F	T
F	F	T	T
F	F	F	T

We see that (1) ⊃ (2) is a tautology, and hence that (2) can be validly inferred from (1). The formula "[p ⊃ (q ⊃ ∼r)] ⊃ [r ⊃ (q ⊃ ∼p)]" is a law of logic.

The truth-table which gives the answer to the second question is:

p	q	r	[p ⊃ (q ⊃ ∼r)] ⊃ [∼q ⊃ (p ⊃ r)]
T	T	T	T
T	T	F	T
T	F	T	T
T	F	F	F
F	T	T	
F	T	F	
F	F	T	
F	F	F	

To determine that (3) cannot validly be inferred from (1) it is not necessary to determine the truth-value of (1) ⊃ (3) beyond the fourth condition. The formula "[p ⊃ (q ⊃ ∼r)] ⊃ [∼q ⊃ (p ⊃ r)]" is not a law of logic.

(b) Given: (1) If Smith is happy, then if he works he does not grumble
    (2) Smith is happy
    (3) He does not grumble.
    What can be inferred as to whether Smith works?

It is not necessary to write the truth-table for this problem in the usual way. A curtailed version consisting of the array of truth-conditions together with the correlated truth-value T for the conjunction of statements suffices for the solution of the problem. The F's may be neglected, since the problem is to determine what follows when the conjunction is *true*. For the answer we go back into the truth-conditions:

p	q	r	[p ⊃ (q ⊃ ∼r)] . p . r
T	T	T	
T	T	F	
T	F	T	T T T
T	F	F	
F	T	T	
F	T	F	
F	F	T	
F	F	F	

We see that the third truth-condition is the only one for which the conjunction of (1), (2), and (3) is true, and this condition shows "q" to be false. Thus the formula "{[p ⊃ (q ⊃ ∼r)] . p . r} ⊃ ∼q" is a tautology, or a law of logic.

The Axiomatic Method

There is a further method for selecting from the total class of truth-function formulas those which are laws of logic. This is the axiomatic method, which introduces order and system into logic. Roughly speaking, the introduction of this method stands to the material of the preceding sections as Euclid's *Elements* stood to geometry in ancient Greece. We have so far noted a few of the laws of logic for calculating conclusions from premises. The axiomatic method is an exact procedure for deducing new laws of logic from premises which are themselves laws of logic. This method makes the order of their occurrence their order of deduction within a system. A most important advantage of the axiomatic method over the matrix method for deciding which statement-forms are laws of logic is that the latter method can only determine this for laws which are truth-functions, whereas the axiomatic method does this and more. From suitable premises it yields laws which are not truth-functions, i.e., laws which are constructed on variables the replacements of which are not statements. An example is the logical law which is exemplified by "If not all perfect numbers are not odd, then some perfect numbers are odd".

The Concept of a Logistic System

In order to develop in a clear-cut way the axiomatic method for deriving truth-function laws, it is required to introduce the reader to the general notion of a logistic system. To put it briefly, a logistic system may be described as an artificial language which, in contrast to natural languages, lists separately its primitive symbols and its defined symbols, lays down rules for deciding which sequences of symbols are to count as syntactically correct sentences, and stipulates what is to constitute a correct derivation or proof. The rules and stipulations in every case must be *effective*, that is, be such that a merely mechanical procedure, without reference to the meanings of the symbols, leaves it undebatable whether a sequence of symbols is properly formed and whether a proof is correct.

The vocabulary of the truth-function calculus will consist of an indefinite list of variables "p", "q", "r", . . . ; the operators "$\sim$" and "v"; and brackets "(", ")". The term "formula" will mean any combination of these. Some combinations will be merely ill-formed sequences of terms, e.g., "v p", "$q \sim$", and hence a syntax or grammar for the logistic system is required to settle which combinations are to count as correctly formed sentences, or as *wellformed formulas*. The language needed to discuss this minimal language is called the *meta-language*. Here it is ordinary English together with the syntactical variables "A", "B", etc., which take wellformed formulas as values. In it we set out the rules for the logistic system. These include *formation rules*, i.e., the syntax for the system, the following being sufficient to generate the entire class of wellformed formulas.

> A variable alone is wellformed
> If A is wellformed, $\sim$(A) is wellformed
> If A and B are wellformed, (A) $\vee$ (B) is wellformed.

No formula is wellformed unless it is constructible by the above rules or is definitionally replaceable by one which is wellformed. It should be noted that although wellformed formulas are such that they yield statements upon substitution of statements for the variables "p", "q", "r", ... in expressions which are values of A, B, ..., and never meaningless combinations of symbols, the formation rules are set out without reference to meanings.

Starting from our primitive symbols and two definitionally introduced symbols "." and "$\supset$", it is readily seen that the formation rules secure that the following formulas are wellformed:

$$\sim(p), \qquad [\sim(p)] \vee (q), \qquad (p) \supset (q), \qquad (p) \cdot (q).$$

The formulas "$[\sim(p)] \vee (q)$" and "$\sim\{[\sim(p)] \vee [\sim(q)]\}$" are derived by the use of the second and third rules, and "$(p) \supset (q)$", "$(p) \cdot (q)$" are obtained from these formulas by definition. The role of brackets is to indicate what is called the *scope* of the operator, i.e., the part or parts of the expression which the operator governs. In "$[\sim(p)] \vee (q)$", "$\sim$" governs, i.e., negates, "(p)", while "$\vee$" governs, i.e., disjoins, "$[\sim(p)]$" and "(q)". In "$\sim[(p) \vee (q)]$" the scope of "$\sim$" is the disjunction "$(p) \vee (q)$", and the scope of "$\vee$" is "(p)", "(q)". Without brackets a formula may fail to be wellformed; thus, it is impossible to say what is the antecedent of "r" in "$p \supset q \supset r$". However, for typographical simplicity we shall dispense with brackets within wellformed formulas if A stands for a single variable or its negation; and except where "$\sim$" prefaces a bracketed expression of more than one variable we shall replace brackets by dots. The following are the conventions for the use of dots: the scope of an operator will extend backward or forward past a lesser number of dots, as in "$p \supset q . \supset . r$", and up to a greater number of dots, as in "$p \supset q . \supset . r : \equiv . s$". Dots used to punctuate will extend past an equal number of dots used to conjoin, as in "$p . \supset . q . r$". And the scope of a single dot used to conjoin will be wider than that of any unpunctuated operator, as in "$p \supset q . r$", read "'$p \supset q$' and 'r' are both true".

Amongst wellformed formulas constructed according to the formation rules, some will be contingent, some inconsistent, and some tautologous. The logistic system to be set out consists solely of formulas of the last class. The axiomatization of this class is accomplished by discovering a small number of tautological formulas from which by the use of certain rules of inference all the remaining tautologies can be derived, and only those. Whitehead and Russell's famous *Principia Mathematica* takes five formulas for its axioms, one of which was proved to be redundant and is omitted here. These, instead of being stated exclusively in terms of "$\sim$" and "$\vee$", are stated with the help of "$\supset$", which is introduced by definition. They are

$$p \vee p . \supset . p$$
$$q . \supset . p \vee q$$
$$p \vee q . \supset . q \vee p$$
$$q \supset r . \supset : p \vee q . \supset . p \vee r.$$

The reader may verify by the matrix method that these are all tautologies, true for any "p", "q", "r". Theorems, all of which are tautologies, are deduced from these by means of two rules of inference within the logistic system. As in the case of the formation rules for wellformed formulas, these *transformation rules* are in the meta-language. They are:

I From A, the result of substituting B for each occurrence of the same variable in A may be inferred (rule of substitution)

II From A and A $\supset$ B, B may be inferred (rule of modus ponens).

The Propositional Calculus

The system for deriving tautologies as set out above is often called the *propositional calculus*. Various alternative sets of axioms have been discovered which serve the same purpose as the *Principia* set, and, as is to be expected, formulas which are axioms in one system appear as theorems in the others, the totality of tautologies thus being the same in each system. One such set, from the Polish logician, J. Łukasiewicz, to be presented at some length here, consists of three axioms stated solely in terms of "$\sim$" and "$\supset$". The rules for the formation of wellformed formulas using "$\sim$" and "$\vee$" are easily restated for "$\sim$" and "$\supset$", and "$\vee$" is definitionally introduced:

$$(A) \vee (B) = Df. \sim(A) \supset (B).$$

The rules of logistic inference are the same as those given above, and their use to deduce theorems will be explained shortly. The axiom set is

(1) $p \supset q . \supset : q \supset r . \supset . p \supset r$

(2) $\sim p \supset p . \supset . p$

(3) $p . \supset . \sim p \supset q$

We proceed now to explain and illustrate the use of the two rules of inference for deriving theorems. The rule of substitution, I, is justified by the fact that a formula's being tautologous is equivalent to its holding for *any* values of its variables, no matter what their form is. Thus, for example, "$p . \supset . \sim p \supset q$" holds for negative statements, implicative statements, disjunctions. This means that the forms of such statements may be substituted for the variables to yield new theorems. It is convenient to write proofs in a set form. The theorem to be proved is stated first, and the demonstration is set out below it. A substitution made on a variable, say "p" for "q" in a formula A, is indicated by writing "$A, \dfrac{p}{q}$". The result of the substitution immediately follows the bracket. We proceed to demonstrate theorems (4) and (5).

(4) $\sim p . \supset . \sim\sim p \supset q$

    (3), $\dfrac{\sim p}{p} \Big]$ $\sim p . \supset . \sim\sim p \supset q$

(5) $p . \supset : \sim p . \supset . p \supset q$

    (3), $\dfrac{p \supset q}{q} \Big]$ $p . \supset : \sim p . \supset . p \supset q$

    Two conditions are placed on substitutions, which if violated give illegitimate results. Substitutions, several of which may be made simultaneously, are on *variables alone*. The same substitution must be made for the same variable throughout. Replacement of one complex expression by another is allowed only when they are definitionally identical. For example, "$p \vee q$", which is by definition the same as "$\sim p \supset q$", can replace "$\sim p \supset q$" in (3) to yield

(6) $p . \supset . p \vee q$

But definitional replacement can be made only of implicative forms having an antecedent prefaced by at least one negation sign, e.g., "$\sim\sim p \supset q$" by "$\sim p \vee q$", but not "$p \supset q$" by "$\sim p \vee q$". Unlike substitution on variables, replacements of this sort need not be made for every occurrence of the expression to be replaced. This is permissible because the interchange of definitional identities merely yields an expression which says the same thing in different terms.

(7) $p . \supset . \sim p \supset p$

(8) $p \vee p . \supset . p$

    (2), Df.] $p \vee p . \supset . p$

(9) $p . \supset . p \vee p$

Formulas (4) through (9) are the first theorems in the system, derived by rule I and the definition. We now illustrate the use of rule II, modus ponens, which allows us to detach a consequent from an implication whose antecedent is an axiom or a proved theorem.

(10) $p \supset p$

$(1), \dfrac{\sim p \supset q}{q}, \dfrac{p}{r} \Big]$

$\qquad\qquad p . \supset . \sim p \supset q : \supset :. \sim p \supset q . \supset . p : \supset . p \supset p$ (a)

$(3), (a), \text{II}] \quad \sim p \supset q . \supset . p : \supset . p \supset p$ (b)

$(b), \dfrac{p}{q} \Big] \quad \sim p \supset p . \supset . p : \supset . p \supset p$ (c)

$(c), (2), \text{II}] \quad p \supset p$

(11) $p \vee \sim p$

$(10), \dfrac{\sim p}{p} \Big] \quad \sim p \supset \sim p$ (a)

$(a), \text{Df.}] \quad p \vee \sim p$

(12) $\sim p \supset p . \supset . \sim p \supset q$

$(1), \dfrac{\sim p \supset p}{p}, \dfrac{p}{q} \Big]$

$\qquad\qquad \sim p \supset p . \supset . p : \supset :. p \supset r . \supset : \sim p \supset p . \supset . r$ (a)

$(2), (a), \text{II}] \quad p \supset r . \supset : \sim p \supset p . \supset . r$ (b)

$(b), \dfrac{\sim p \supset q}{r} \Big] \quad p . \supset . \sim p \supset q : \supset : \sim p \supset p . \supset . \sim p \supset q$ (c)

$(3), (c), \text{II}] \quad \sim p \supset p . \supset . \sim p \supset q$

Of the theorems that follow, a number are stated without proof. Their proof will provide an exercise for the reader, and in some cases hints as to procedure are given.

(13) $p \vee p . \supset . p \vee q$

(14) $\sim p \supset q . \supset . \sim q \supset q : \supset : p . \supset . \sim q \supset q$
HINT: In (1) put $\sim p \supset q$ for q, $\sim q \supset q$ for r, and use (3)

(15) $\sim q \supset \sim p . \supset : p . \supset . \sim q \supset q$
HINT: In (1) put $\sim q \supset \sim p$ for p, $\sim p \supset q . \supset . \sim q \supset q$ for q,
$p . \supset . \sim q \supset q$ for r
In (1) put $\sim q$ for p, $\sim p$ for q, q for r. Use II, then (14)

(16) $\sim q \supset \sim p . \supset :. \sim q \supset q . \supset . q : \supset . p \supset q$
HINT: In (1) put $\sim q \supset \sim p$ for p, $p . \supset . \sim q \supset q$ for q, $\sim q \supset q .$
$\supset . q : \supset . p \supset q$ for r. Use (15) and II
In (1) put $\sim q \supset q$ for q, q for r

(17) $q . \supset :. \sim q \supset q . \supset . q : \supset . p \supset q$

   HINT: In (1) put q for p, $\sim q \supset \sim p$ for q, $\sim q \supset q . \supset . q : \supset . p \supset q$
        for r. Use (3), II, (16)

(18) $p . \supset : \sim q \supset q . \supset . q$

   HINT: In (17) put $\sim q \supset q . \supset . q$ for q
        In (2) put q for p, use II
        In (2) put $\sim q \supset q . \supset . q$ for p, use II

(19) $\sim q \supset q . \supset . q : \supset . p \supset q :. \supset : \sim (p \supset q) . \supset . p \supset q$

   HINT: In (1) put $\sim (p \supset q)$ for p, $\sim q \supset q . \supset . q$ for q, $p \supset q$ for r
        In (18) put $\sim (p \supset q)$ for p, use II

(20) $\sim q \supset q . \supset . q : \supset . p \supset q :. \supset . p \supset q$

   HINT: In (1) put $\sim q \supset q . \supset . q : \supset . p \supset q$ for p, $\sim (p \supset q) . \supset$
        $. p \supset q$ for q, $p \supset q$ for r. Use (19) and II
        In (2) put $p \supset q$ for p

(21) $q . \supset . p \supset q$

   $(1), \dfrac{q}{p}, \dfrac{\sim q \supset q . \supset . q : \supset . p \supset q}{q}, \dfrac{p \supset q}{r} \Big]$

                $(17) . \supset :. (20) . \supset : q . \supset . p \supset q$ (a)

   (17), (20), (a), II twice] $q . \supset . p \supset q$

(22) $q . \supset . p \vee q$

(23) $\sim q \supset \sim p . \supset . p \supset q$

   $(1), \dfrac{\sim q \supset \sim p}{p}, \dfrac{\sim q \supset q . \supset . q : \supset . p \supset q}{q}, \dfrac{p \supset q}{r} \Big]$

                $(16) . \supset . (20) \supset (23)$ (a)

   (16), (20), (a), II twice] $\sim q \supset \sim p . \supset . p \supset q$

(24) $\sim p . \supset . p \supset q$

   $(1), \dfrac{\sim p}{p}, \dfrac{\sim q \supset \sim p}{q}, \dfrac{p \supset q}{r} \Big]$

      $\sim p . \supset . \sim q \supset \sim p : \supset :.$
               $\sim q \supset \sim p . \supset . p \supset q : \supset : \sim p . \supset . p \supset q$ (a)

   $(21), \dfrac{\sim q}{p}, \dfrac{\sim p}{q} \Big]$ $\sim p . \supset . \sim q \supset p$ (b)

   (23), (a), (b), II twice] $\sim p . \supset . p \supset q$

(25) $p \supset q . \supset . p : \supset . p$

   $(21), \dfrac{p \supset q . \supset . p}{p}, \dfrac{p}{q} \Big]$ $p . \supset :. p \supset q . \supset . p : \supset . p$ (a)

$(1), \dfrac{q}{p}, \dfrac{p \supset q}{q} \Big]$ $q . \supset . p \supset q : \supset : . p \supset q . \supset . r : \supset . q \supset r$ (b)

$(21), (b), II]$ $p \supset q . \supset . r : \supset . q \supset r$ (c)

$(c), \dfrac{p \supset q . \supset . p}{q}, \dfrac{p}{r} \Big]$

$\quad p . \supset : p \supset q . \supset . p : . \supset . p :: \supset : . p \supset q . \supset . p : \supset . p$ (d)

$(a), (d), II]$ $p \supset q . \supset . p : \supset . p$

(26) $\sim\sim p \supset p$

$(1), \dfrac{\sim p}{p}, \dfrac{p \supset q}{q} \Big]$

$\qquad\qquad \sim p . \supset . p \supset q : \supset : . p \supset q . \supset . r : \supset . \sim p \supset r$ (a)

$(24), (a), II]$ $p \supset q . \supset . r : \supset . \sim p \supset r$ (b)

$(b), \dfrac{\sim p}{p}, \dfrac{p}{q}, \dfrac{p}{r} \Big]$ $\sim p \supset p . \supset . p : \supset . \sim\sim p \supset p$ (c)

$(2), (c), II]$ $\sim\sim p \supset p$

(27) $\sim p \lor p$

(28) $\sim\sim q . \supset . p \supset q$

$(1), \dfrac{\sim p}{p}, \dfrac{p \supset q}{q} \Big]$

$\qquad\qquad \sim p . \supset . p \supset q : \supset : . p \supset q . \supset . r : \supset . \sim p \supset r$ (a)

$(24), (a), II]$ $p \supset q . \supset . r : \supset . \sim p \supset r$ (b)

$(b), \dfrac{\sim q}{p}, \dfrac{\sim p}{q}, \dfrac{p \supset q}{r} \Big]$

$\qquad\qquad \sim q \supset \sim p . \supset . p \supset q : \supset : \sim\sim q . \supset . p \supset q$ (c)

$(23), (c), II]$ $\sim\sim q . \supset . p \supset q$

(29) $\sim(p \supset q) . \supset . p$

$(1), \dfrac{\sim p}{p}, \dfrac{p \supset q}{q} \Big]$

$\qquad\qquad \sim p . \supset . p \supset q : \supset : . p \supset q . \supset . r : \supset . \sim p \supset r$ (a)

$(24), (a), II]$ $p \supset q . \supset . r : \supset . \sim p \supset r$ (b)

$(b), \dfrac{p \supset q}{p}, \dfrac{p}{q}, \dfrac{p}{r} \Big]$

$\qquad\qquad p \supset q . \supset . p : \supset . p : . \supset : \sim(p \supset q) . \supset . p$ (c)

$(25), (c), II]$ $\sim(p \supset q) . \supset . p$

(30) $p \supset q . \supset . p : \supset . q \supset p$

HINT: In (1) put $p \supset q . \supset . p$ for p, p for q, $q \supset p$ for r. Use (25), (21)

(31) $p . \supset . p \supset q : \supset . p \supset q$

    HINT: In (1) put $p \supset q$ for q, q for r

               In (25) put $p \supset q$ for p

               In (1) put $p . \supset . p \supset q$ for p, $p \supset q . \supset . q : \supset . p \supset q$ for q, $p \supset q$ for r

(32) $p . \supset : p \supset q . \supset . q$

    HINT: In (1) put $p \supset q$ for p, p for q, q for r

               In (31) put $p \supset q$ for p

               In (1) put $p \supset q . \supset . p$ for p, $p \supset q . \supset : p \supset q . \supset . q$ for q, $p \supset q . \supset . q$ for r

               In (21) put $p \supset q$ for p, p for q

               In (1) put $p \supset q . \supset . p$ for q, $p \supset q . \supset . q$ for r

(33) $p . \supset . q \supset r : \supset : q . \supset . p \supset r$

    (1), $\dfrac{p \supset q . \supset . q}{q}\bigg]$

    $p . \supset : p \supset q . \supset . q : . \supset :: p \supset q . \supset . q : \supset . r : . \supset . p \supset r$ (a)

    (a), (32), II] $p \supset q . \supset . q : \supset . r : . \supset . p \supset r$ (b)

    (b), $\dfrac{q}{p} , \dfrac{r}{q} , \dfrac{p \supset r}{r}\bigg]$ $q \supset r . \supset . r : \supset . p \supset r : . \supset : q . \supset . p \supset r$ (c)

    (1), $\dfrac{q \supset r}{q}\bigg]$ $p . \supset . q \supset r : \supset : . q \supset r . \supset . r : \supset . p \supset r$ (d)

    (1), $\dfrac{p . \supset . q \supset r}{p} , \dfrac{q \supset r . \supset . r : \supset . p \supset r}{q} , \dfrac{q . \supset . p \supset r}{r}\bigg]$

               (d) $. \supset :: (c) . \supset : . p . \supset . q \supset r . \supset : q . \supset . p \supset r$ (e)

    (d), (c), (e), II twice] $p . \supset . q \supset r : \supset : q . \supset . p \supset r$

(34) $q \supset r . \supset : p \supset q . \supset . p \supset r$

    (33), $\dfrac{p \supset q}{p} , \dfrac{q \supset r}{q} , \dfrac{p \supset r}{r}\bigg]$ $p \supset q . \supset : q \supset r . \supset . p \supset r : . \supset : .$

                                  $q \supset r . \supset : p \supset q . \supset . p \supset r$ (a)

    (1), (a), II] $q \supset r . \supset : p \supset q . \supset . p \supset r$

(35) $q \supset r . \supset : p \vee q . \supset . p \vee r$

    (34), $\dfrac{\sim p}{p}$, Df.$\bigg]$ $q \supset r . \supset : p \vee q . \supset . p \vee r$

(36) $q \supset \sim p . \supset . p \supset \sim q$

    (1), $\dfrac{\sim \sim q}{p} , \dfrac{\sim p}{r}\bigg]$ $\sim \sim q \supset q . \supset : q \supset \sim p . \supset . \sim \sim q \supset \sim p$ (a)

(26), (a), II] $\quad q \supset \sim p \,.\, \supset \,.\, \sim\sim q \supset \sim p$ $\hfill$ (b)

(34), $\dfrac{q \supset \sim p}{p}\,,\; \dfrac{\sim\sim q \supset \sim p}{q}\,,\; \dfrac{p \supset \sim q}{r}\Big]$

$\qquad \sim\sim q \supset \sim p \,.\, \supset \,.\, p \supset \sim q :\, \supset :.\, q \supset \sim p \,.\, \supset \,.\, \sim\sim q \supset \sim p :$
$\qquad\qquad\qquad\qquad\qquad\qquad\quad \supset :\, q \supset \sim p \,.\, \supset \,.\, p \supset \sim q$ $\hfill$ (c)

(23), $\dfrac{\sim q}{q}\Big] \quad \sim\sim q \supset \sim p \,.\, \supset \,.\, p \supset \sim q$ $\hfill$ (d)

(d), (c), II] $\quad q \supset \sim p \,.\, \supset \,.\, \sim\sim q \supset \sim p :\, \supset :\, q \supset \sim p \,.\, \supset\,.$
$\qquad\qquad\qquad\qquad\qquad\qquad\qquad\qquad\qquad\qquad p \supset \sim q$ $\hfill$ (e)

(b), (e), II] $\quad q \supset \sim p \,.\, \supset \,.\, p \supset \sim q$

(37) $p \supset \sim\sim p$
$\quad$ HINT: Use (36), (10)

(38) $p \supset q \,.\, \supset \,.\, \sim q \supset \sim p$

$\quad$ (34), $\dfrac{\sim\sim q}{r}\Big] \quad q \supset \sim\sim q \,.\, \supset :\, p \supset q \,.\, \supset \,.\, p \supset \sim\sim q$ $\hfill$ (a)

$\quad$ (37), (a), II] $\quad p \supset q \,.\, \supset \,.\, p \supset \sim\sim q$ $\hfill$ (b)

$\quad$ (36), $\dfrac{\sim q}{p}\,,\; \dfrac{p}{q}\Big] \quad p \supset \sim\sim q \,.\, \supset \,.\, \sim q \supset \sim p$ $\hfill$ (c)

$\quad$ (1), $\dfrac{p \supset q}{p}\,,\; \dfrac{p \supset \sim\sim q}{q}\,,\; \dfrac{\sim q \supset \sim p}{r}\Big] \quad$ (b) $\,.\, \supset :.\, $ (c) $\,.\, \supset :\, p \supset q\,.$
$\qquad\qquad\qquad\qquad\qquad\qquad\qquad\qquad\qquad\qquad \supset \,.\, \sim q \supset \sim p$ $\hfill$ (d)

$\quad$ (b), (c), II twice] $\quad p \supset q \,.\, \supset \,.\, \sim q \supset \sim p$

(39) $\sim p \supset q \,.\, \supset \,.\, \sim q \supset p$

$\quad$ (34), $\dfrac{\sim p}{p}\,,\; \dfrac{\sim\sim q}{r}\Big] \quad q \supset \sim\sim q \,.\, \supset :\, \sim p \supset q \,.\, \supset \,.\, \sim p \supset \sim\sim q$ $\hfill$ (a)

$\quad$ (37), (a), II] $\quad \sim p \supset q \,.\, \supset \,.\, \sim p \supset \sim\sim q$ $\hfill$ (b)

$\quad$ (36), $\dfrac{\sim q}{p}\,,\; \dfrac{\sim p}{q}\Big] \quad \sim p \supset \sim\sim q \,.\, \supset \,.\, \sim q \supset \sim\sim p$ $\hfill$ (c)

$\quad$ (34), $\dfrac{\sim q}{p}\,,\; \dfrac{\sim\sim p}{q}\,,\; \dfrac{p}{r}\Big] \quad \sim\sim p \supset p \,.\, \supset :\, \sim q \supset \sim\sim p\,.$
$\qquad\qquad\qquad\qquad\qquad\qquad\qquad\qquad\qquad\quad \supset \,.\, \sim q \supset p$ $\hfill$ (d)

$\quad$ (26), (d), II] $\quad \sim q \supset \sim\sim p \,.\, \supset \,.\, \sim q \supset p$ $\hfill$ (e)

$\quad$ (1), $\dfrac{\sim p \supset q}{p}\,,\; \dfrac{\sim p \supset \sim\sim q}{q}\,,\; \dfrac{\sim q \supset \sim\sim p}{r}\Big]$

$\qquad\qquad\qquad$ (b) $\,.\, \supset :.\, $ (c) $\,.\, \supset :\, \sim p \supset q \,.\, \supset \,.\, \sim q \supset \sim\sim p$ $\hfill$ (f)
$\quad$ (b), (c), II] $\quad \sim p \supset q \,.\, \supset \,.\, \sim q \supset \sim\sim p$ $\hfill$ (g)

$$(1), \; \frac{\sim p \supset q}{p}, \; \frac{\sim q \supset \sim\sim p}{q}, \; \frac{\sim q \supset p}{r} \Big]$$

(g) $\;.\supset :.$ (e) $.\supset :\sim p \supset q . \supset . \sim q \supset p$ (h)

(h), (g), (e), II twice] $\;\sim p \supset q . \supset . \sim q \supset p$

(40) $p \supset \sim p . \supset . \sim p$

$$(34), \; \frac{r}{p}, \; \frac{\sim p \supset p}{q}, \; \frac{p}{r} \Big] \quad \sim p \supset p . \supset . p : \supset :. r . \supset . \sim p \supset p :$$
$$\supset . r \supset p \quad \text{(a)}$$

(2), (a), II] $\;r . \supset . \sim p \supset p : \supset . r \supset p$ (b)

$$(b), \; \frac{\sim p}{p}, \; \frac{p \supset \sim p}{r} \Big] \quad p \supset \sim p . \supset . \sim\sim p \supset \sim p : \supset : p \supset \sim p .$$
$$\supset . \sim p \quad \text{(c)}$$

$$(38), \; \frac{\sim p}{q} \Big] \quad p \supset \sim p . \supset . \sim\sim p \supset \sim p \quad \text{(d)}$$

(d), (c), II] $\;p \supset \sim p . \supset . \sim p$

(41) $p \vee q . \supset . q \vee p$

(39), Df.] $\;p \vee q . \supset . q \vee p$

Properties of the Postulate Set

With the last theorem, together with theorems (8), (22), and (35), we have proved or have indicated the proofs of all the postulates of the calculus of *Principia Mathematica*. And it is in fact the case that the latter postulates are adequate for proof of those of the present system. Our proofs might have been simplified if we had first derived from the two rules of inference a further rule, the so-called *deduction theorem*. But such a derivation lies beyond the scope of this introduction to logic. The proofs of two important properties of the set of postulates, namely, that it is *consistent* and *complete*, cannot be gone into here either. To prove consistency of the present set is to show that there is no wellformed formula A such that both A and $\sim$A are provable. To prove completeness is to show that any wellformed formula A is either itself a theorem or its addition renders the set inconsistent. Showing this is equivalent to demonstrating that the postulates are adequate for the derivation of every tautology, including those expressed in terms of "." and "$\equiv$", once these symbols are introduced by definitions. The two *meta-theorems*, that every tautology is a theorem and that every theorem is a tautology, together with the fact that in the matrix method we have an effective procedure for deciding in the case of every truth-function whether it is a tautology, provides us with a solution of the so-called *decision problem*. This is the problem of finding an effective procedure for deciding whether any given formula is a theorem of the system. In the case of the logistic system we call attention to in Part II this problem cannot be solved. Another, relatively unimportant, property of our present set is that it is *independent*, that is, that no postulate is derivable from any combination of the others.

EXERCISES

1. Re-express each of the following (a) in terms of "v" and "∼", (b) in terms of "." and "∼", (c) in terms of "⊃" and "∼":

$$p \equiv (q \supset r), \qquad \sim p \supset [\sim q \, . \, (r \vee s)].$$

2. Carry out the indicated process of negating until no negation sign remains outside any pair of brackets:

$$\sim[\sim p \supset (\sim r \, . \, t)], \quad \sim\{(p) \supset [(q \equiv r) \vee \sim s]\}. \quad \sim\{p \supset [(q \, . \, \sim r) \supset (s \supset \sim t)]\}.$$

3. Show which of the following are equivalent and which are not:

$$(p \, . \, q) \supset r, \quad (p \, . \, \sim r) \supset \sim q, \quad (\sim p \supset q) \supset r, \quad r \supset (\sim p \, . \, \sim q).$$

4. Express the exclusive sense of "or" in terms of "∼", "v", and ".", and in terms of "∼" and "v" only.

5. (a) Given: 1. If it is true both that Diogenes is a cynic and does not like human beings or else true that he likes to call attention to himself, then he is an irritating person
    2. If he does not like to call attention to himself, then his search for an honest man is not a sham
    3. He is not an irritating person.
    What, if anything, can be inferred (1) as to whether his search for an honest man is a sham, (2) as to whether he is a cynic?
  (b) Given: 1. If Francis Bacon wrote "Hamlet", then if Shakespeare was a great intellectual, he was the author of "New Atlantis"
    2. If Shakespeare was a great intellectual, then he had deep insight into human nature and he was not given to fanciful speculations about utopias
    3. If Shakespeare had deep insight into human nature, he was not the author of "New Atlantis"
    4. Shakespeare was a great intellectual.
    Question: Did Francis Bacon write "Hamlet"?
  (c) Given: 1. Either Demetrius, Gregory, or Stepan stole the necklace
    2. If Gregory stole the necklace, then if Lady Mayfair was at the masked ball, then Gregory's beautiful accomplice was also there
    3. If Gregory's beautiful accomplice was at the masked ball, Inspector Bull saw her
    4. If Lady Mayfair was at the masked ball, then Inspector Bull was present and watchful
    5. If Inspector Bull was present and watchful, he did not see Gregory's beautiful accomplice
    6. Lady Mayfair was at the masked ball
    7. If Inspector Bull was present and watchful, Demetrius did not steal the necklace.
    Question: Who stole the necklace?

6. Which of the following are valid, and which are invalid?

$$\frac{\begin{array}{c}p \supset (q \supset r)\\ p \, . \sim r\end{array}}{\sim q}, \qquad \frac{\begin{array}{c}(p \supset q) \supset (r \, . \, s)\\ \sim s\end{array}}{p \, \text{v} \sim q \, \text{v} \, r}, \qquad \frac{\begin{array}{c}\sim p \supset (q \supset \sim r)\\ r\end{array}}{p},$$

$$\frac{\begin{array}{c}(p \, \text{v} \sim q) \, \text{v} \, (r \equiv s)\\ \sim p \, . \, q\end{array}}{\sim r \, \text{v} \, s}, \qquad \frac{\begin{array}{c}\sim[(p \equiv \sim q) \, . \, (r \, . \, s)]\\ p \, . \sim q\end{array}}{\sim r}.$$

7. Give the truth tables for

$$(p \supset q) \supset [p \supset (\sim q \supset r)], \qquad p \, . \sim[q \supset (r \supset q)], \qquad p \, \text{v} \sim[q \supset (r \supset q)],$$
$$\sim\{(p \equiv \sim q) \equiv [(p \supset \sim q) \, . \, (\sim p \supset q)]\}.$$

Which is tautologous, which contingent, and which contradictory?

8. Duality: The dual of a truth-function formula F is obtained by interchanging conjunction and disjunction throughout F, i.e., by replacing A . B everywhere by A v B and A v B by A . B. Thus, the dual of "$\sim(p \, \text{v} \, q \, \text{v} \sim r \, . \sim s)$" is "$\sim(p \, . \, q \, . \sim r \, . \, \text{v} \, . \sim s)$", the dual of "$(p \, . \sim q \, . \, \text{v} \, . \, r) \, \text{v} \sim(\sim s \, . \, t)$" is "$(p \, \text{v} \sim q \, . \, r) \, . \sim(\sim s \, \text{v} \, t)$". The dual of "$p \supset q$" is "$\sim p \, . \, q$", of "$p \supset q \, . \supset . \, r \, . \, s$" is "$\sim(\sim p \, . \, q) \, . \, r \, \text{v} \, s$".

State the duals of:

$$p \, \text{v} \sim(q \, . \sim r \, . \, \text{v} \, . \, s \supset t), \qquad \sim p \, . \supset : q \, . \equiv . \, r \, . \, s, \qquad q \supset r \, . \supset : p \, \text{v} \, q \, . \supset . \, p \, \text{v} \, r.$$

Is the negation of the dual of a tautology itself a tautology?

$$p \supset \sim q \, . \supset . \, q \supset \sim p, \qquad q \supset r \, . \supset : p \supset q \, . \supset . \, p \supset r.$$

Is the negation of the dual of a contradiction itself a contradiction?

$$p \, . \, r : p \supset \sim r, \qquad \sim(p \, . \, q \, . \supset . \, p \supset q).$$

[II]

Quantification

Inferences which are made in terms of the ideas discussed in Part I do not exhaust all possible inferences. The following inferences will readily be seen to be formal, and they involve further terms not definable by our earlier terms. Given the premises

> If anyone is a gambler, then he likes to handle money

and

> There is someone who is a gambler and is not avaricious,

we may infer the conclusion

> There is someone who is not avaricious but likes to handle money.

And from the single premise,

> Some even numbers are less than every number greater than the smallest odd prime,

we may infer

> It is not the case that for every even number x there is a number which is greater than the smallest odd prime and not greater than x.

An examination of these two deductions makes it clear that their validity hinges on more than just the terms "$\sim$", "$\supset$", etc. The terms "any", "every", "there is", "some" also play a role, and are terms which occur as parts of formal statement-forms, i.e., they are themselves formal terms. In fact "every" and "some" were used in Part I, but not in an explicit way. Saying that "$q \supset . p \supset q$" has *universal validity* and that "$\sim q \supset . p \supset q$" does not are other ways of saying, without explicitly heralding the terms "every" and "some", that *every* substitution on "p" and "q" in "$q \supset . p \supset q$" yields a truth, and that *some* substitutions on "$\sim q \supset . p \supset q$" do not yield truths. But there is an important difference between the use of these terms in connection with the statement-forms explicated in Part I and their use in the above two examples. In "for every $p, q, q \supset . p \supset q$" and in "for some $p, q, \sim q \supset . p \supset q$", "every" and "some" operate on terms within

29

statement-forms which are themselves statement-forms, whereas in the above two examples the terms within the statement-forms on which they operate are not themselves statement-forms. Of these terms no mention either explicit or implicit has yet been made. How the operators "every", "any", "some", called *quantifiers*, function remains to be explained.

The Universal Quantifier

Compare the statements

If Vladimir is a gambler, then Vladimir likes to handle money
If anyone is a gambler, he likes to handle money.

The difference between them is obviously one of generality. The second is a generalization of which the first is a concrete instance. How the two are related can best be seen by replacing the proper name in the first by a row of dots, to obtain

If . . is a gambler, then . . . likes to handle money.

The components of this form, ". . . is a gambler", ". . . likes to handle money", are statement-forms, although not formal ones; and they are not truth-functions. If the non-formal terms "gambler" and "likes to handle money" are deleted, the result is a statement-form made up of statement-forms the components of which are not statement-forms. In fact we have arrived at a kind of formula which uses two new and different types of variables, called *individual* variables and *predicate* or *functional* variables. The formula ". . . is - - -" is a form possessed in common by a whole assemblage of statements:

Vladimir is a gambler
Jones is avaricious
Pascal is a mystic.

The standard convention for representing the form of these is to use the letters "x", "y", "z", . . . as individual variables and "f", "g", "h", . . . as functional variables. The formula ". . . is - - -" becomes "x is f", which is written

$$fx.$$

Writing the form of "Vladimir is a gambler" as "fx" and of "Vladimir likes to handle money" as "gx", the form of "If Vladimir is a gambler, then Vladimir (is a person who) likes to handle money" becomes

(1) $fx \supset gx.$

The form of "If anyone is a gambler, then he likes to handle money" can now be seen to be a generalization on the same formula, (1), of which "If Vladimir is a gambler, he likes to handle money" is an instance or specification. The generalization is (1) prefaced by the so-called *universal quantifier* "(x)", and written

$$(2) \quad (x)(fx \supset gx).$$

In (1) the variable "x" (and also "f" and "g") is not prefaced by a quantifier and is said to be *free*. Given that "f" and "g" are fixed, substitutions made on "x" will yield a variety of statements. In (2), however, "x" is quantified and is said to be *bound*. No substitutions may be made on "x" when "x" is quantified.

The statements of the following list are taken by logicians to be equivalent in import to "If anyone is a gambler, he likes to handle money", and therefore are counted as exemplifying formula (2):

> For any x, if x is a gambler, x likes to handle money
> Every gambler likes to handle money
> Each gambler likes to handle money
> All gamblers like to handle money.

The Existential Quantifier

Consider the pair of statements

> Vladimir is a gambler
> There is at least one gambler.

Again, as in the case of the first pair of statements, the difference between these two is one of generality: the first conveys more specific information than the second. Along with the second the following statements are taken by logicians to be equivalent in import:

> There is an x such that x is a gambler
> There exists at least one gambler
> Some x's are such that x is a gambler
> Someone is a gambler
> Gamblers exist
> There are gamblers.

The form of each of these is

> There is an x such that fx,

or equivalently,

> Some x's are such that fx.

Logicians replace both "there is an x" and "for some x's" by the symbol "$(\exists x)$", and give as the form of the above statements

$$(\exists x)fx.$$

All of them are restricted generalizations on the formal function "fx", of which "Vladimir is a gambler" is a concrete instance. "$(\exists x)$" is called the *existential quantifier*. Like the universal quantifier, it binds the variable "x" in any formula "fx" falling within its scope.

It might be supposed that the formal function generalized by the universal and existential quantifiers in "All f's are g" and "Some f's are g" is in each case an implicative, or *conditional*. That is, it might be thought that the form of "Some gamblers are avaricious" is given by "$(\exists x)(fx \supset gx)$", just as that of "All gamblers are avaricious" is given by "$(x)(fx \supset gx)$". But this is a mistake. The formula "$(\exists x)(fx \supset gx)$", which says that there is an x such that *if x is f, x is g*, could be true if nothing were f. However, "Some gamblers are avaricious" states that there are gamblers, and it is thus to the effect that there is someone who is both a gambler and avaricious. Its form is rendered by

$$(\exists x)(fx \cdot gx).$$

Just as in ordinary usage "and" has more than one sense (e.g., in "You steal and you will be arrested" it has the sense of "If you steal you will be arrested"), so the verb "are" has a number of senses, two of which are given by "$\supset$" and ".".

A statement to the effect that no f's are g denies that there is something which is both f and g, that is, it is the negation of "$(\exists x)(fx \cdot gx)$". Like "Some f's are g", it is also a generalization upon a conjunction:

$$\sim(\exists x)(fx \cdot gx).$$

The following statements are regarded by logicians as being synonymous, and hence as exemplifying "$\sim(\exists x)(fx \cdot gx)$":

No gamblers are wealthy
Nothing is a gambler and wealthy
There does not exist an x such that x is a gambler and x is wealthy
There are no gamblers who are wealthy
Wealthy gamblers do not exist.

It is to be noted that the scope of "$\sim$" in the above schema is the entire expression. The difference between "No gamblers are wealthy" and "Some gamblers are not wealthy" is that the scope of "$\sim$" in the second statement is merely "x is wealthy":

$$(\exists x)(fx \cdot \sim gx).$$

Further, whereas the first denies the existence of a wealthy gambler, the second asserts the existence of a non-wealthy gambler. In ordinary English the scope of "not" is often ambiguous unless the context of the statement is given. For example, "All women are not ambitious" is open to either of the two interpretations: "*Not all* women are ambitious" (i.e., "*some* are *not* ambitious") and "*No* women are ambitious". On the first interpretation its form is given by the above formulation. On the second interpretation its form is given by "$\sim(\exists x)(fx . gx)$", and equally by

$$(x)(fx \supset \sim gx),$$

read "all f's are non-g". It is intuitively obvious that "No women are ambitious" and "All women are non-ambitious" say the same thing.

The Categorical Statement-forms

The four statement-forms, "All f's are g", "No f's are g", "Some f's are g", and "Some f's are not g", were treated as fundamental in traditional logic and were assigned special names supposedly descriptive of their logical features. They were customarily designated by the letters A, E, I, O, the first two vowels in "affirmo" designating the "affirmative" forms, the two in "nego" designating the "negative" forms.

A, universal affirmative	$(x)(fx \supset gx)$
E, universal negative	$\sim(\exists x)(fx . gx)$
I, particular affirmative	$(\exists x)(fx . gx)$
O, particular negative	$(\exists x)(fx . \sim gx)$.

Statements of these four forms were called *categorical*, by which was meant that they unqualifiedly affirm or deny a predicate of a subject, although, as modern analysis shows, they are not subject-predicate statements. The I and O forms will be recognized as quantified conjunctions of terms. And the A is a universally quantified conditional, the relation between its terms being implication rather than predication. The E form of statement is most naturally read as the negation of a quantified conjunction, but as will be shown later it can be rewritten as a quantified conditional.

In connection with the A form of statement it is of some importance to see how the associated "only if . . ." form of statement is to be written: "(x) (only if fx then gx)". When the A form "(x) (if fx then gx)" holds, "fx" is said to be a sufficient condition for "gx". In turn "gx" is said to be a necessary condition for "fx": "(x) (if $\sim gx$ then $\sim fx$)". Hence to state that "fx" is a necessary condition for "gx" we write "(x) (if $\sim fx$ then $\sim gx$)"; and "(x) (only if fx then gx)", or "only f's are g", may be expressed in our notation

$$(x)(\sim fx \supset \sim gx).$$

34 QUANTIFICATION

To state that "*fx*" is both a necessary and a sufficient condition for "*gx*", for all values of "*x*", we write

$$(x)(fx \supset gx \mathbin{.} \sim\!fx \supset \sim\!gx),$$

which becomes

$$(x)(fx \equiv gx).$$

The Square of Opposition

Statements of the A, E, I, and O forms were thought to stand to each other in a number of logical relations given by what was called the *square of opposition*. A and E statements were considered *contraries*, i.e., such that they could be jointly false but not jointly true. I and O statements were asserted to be *subcontraries*, i.e., such that they could be jointly true but not jointly false. The pairs, A and O, E and I, were taken to be *contradictories*, which under all conditions have opposite truth-values. Finally, A was held to be *superimplicant* to I, and E to O, by which is meant that A implies I, and E implies O, but that the converse in each case fails to hold. The traditional square was given in the form

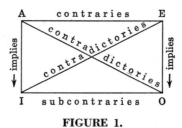

FIGURE 1.

Of the various relations asserted to hold on this square, the following are of special importance:

(1) A ≡ ∼O,   E ≡ ∼I

and

(2) A ⊃ I,   E ⊃ O.

These two sets of relations turn out to be inconsistent with each other, and locating the source of the inconsistency shows two things: (1) that the traditional square is a composite of two squares, and (2) that A and E statements, taken as the contradictories of the corresponding I's and O's, can be jointly true.

It may, to begin with, be somewhat unnatural to think of A and E possibly being true together. But it is entirely natural to suppose that statements of the I and O forms, that is, statements to the effect that there is something which is both f and g, and statements to the effect that there is something which is both f and not g, imply statements of the form "Something is f": $I \supset (\exists x)fx$, $O \supset (\exists x)fx$. For example, the statements "Some flowers are perennials" and "Some flowers are not perennials" both plainly imply that there are flowers. If, however, in conformity with (2), a statement of the A form is taken to imply a corresponding statement of the I form, and the same for E and O, then by the truth-function tautology "$p \supset q . q \supset r : \supset . p \supset r$", both A and E will imply "$(\exists x)fx$". We then have the following conjunction of implications:

$$A \supset (\exists x)fx . E \supset (\exists x)fx . I \supset (\exists x)fx . O \supset (\exists x)fx.$$

According to (1), at least one (in fact exactly two) of the antecedents of this set of implications will be true, and since "$(\exists x)fx$" is a consequent of each of the antecedents, it will have to be true. The argument can be written in the following form:

$$\frac{A \supset (\exists x)fx . E \supset (\exists x)fx . I \supset (\exists x)fx . O \supset (\exists x)fx}{A \quad v \quad E \quad v \quad I \quad v \quad O} .$$
$$(\exists x)fx$$

It is not difficult to see that this consequence lands us in an absurdity. This is that any statement of the form "$(\exists x)fx$" is provable by logic alone, and its denial "$\sim(\exists x)fx$" disprovable by logic alone. For since it is a consequence of each of a pair of contradictory statements, one of which must be true, it will have to be true under all possible conditions, and its denial will have to be false under all possible conditions. It will be recognized, of course, that statements like "Ghosts exist" and "Something is a whale" can have either of *two* truth-values, and similarly for the statements "Ghosts do not exist" and "Nothing is a whale". If we take this fact into account and allow, as logical sanity requires, that statements of the form "$\sim(\exists x)fx$" could, possibly, be true, contradictions break out in the traditional square. By the truth-function tautology "$p \supset q . \sim q . \supset . \sim p$", we see that each of the following is valid:

$$A \supset (\exists x)fx . \sim(\exists x)fx . \supset . \sim A$$
$$E \supset (\exists x)fx . \sim(\exists x)fx . \supset . \sim E.$$

Hence,

$$\frac{A \supset (\exists x)fx . E \supset (\exists x)fx . I \supset (\exists x)fx . O \supset (\exists x)fx}{\sim(\exists x)fx} .$$
$$\sim A . \sim E . \sim I . \sim O$$

The contradictions can perhaps be seen most clearly if $\sim O$ and $\sim I$ are replaced by their equivalents, A and E, when the last line becomes

$$\sim A . \sim E . E . A.$$

It is evident that allowing the possibility of statements of the form
"$\sim(\exists x)fx$" being true entails a contradiction only if both sets of relations
(1) and (2) hold for the same quadruplets of statements. If one of the
set is dropped no contradiction results. The conjunction of "$\sim(\exists x)fx$"
with (1) implies no contradiction unless (2) is added to the conjunction,
and its conjunction with (2) implies no contradiction unless (1) is added.
This would seem to show that the traditional square is really a composite
of two squares, one of which consists of the diagonals and the other of
the sides. These when superimposed on each other generate a contradiction.

Taken as the *contradictory* of O, A does not imply I, and taken as
the *superimplicant* of I, it is not the contradictory of O. Similarly for E
with respect to its related I and O. Thus the A form that implies I cannot
be the same as the A form that is the contradictory of O. The $\sim$O form,
to the effect that there does not exist something which is f and not g, does
not imply the corresponding I, although $\sim$O conjoined with "$(\exists x)fx$" does
imply I. Consequently the A form which implies the I is a conjunction
of the contradictory of O with "$(\exists x)fx$". The so-called A form thus turns
out to be a composite of two A forms: one the simple $\sim$O, the logical
force of which is to deny existence, and the other, $\sim$O in conjunction with
"$(\exists x)fx$". The same consideration applies to the composite E on the
square of opposition. In modern logic A is taken to be $\sim$O and E to be
$\sim$I, and what may be called the conjunctive A and E are assigned no
special code letters.

Statements of the A, E, I, and O types can now be equivalently
written in two ways:

A, $(x)(fx \supset gx)$ $\sim$O, $\sim(\exists x)(fx . \sim gx)$
E, $(x)(fx \supset \sim gx)$ $\sim$I, $\sim(\exists x)(fx . gx)$
I, $(\exists x)(fx . gx)$ $\sim$E, $\sim(x)(fx \supset \sim gx)$
O, $(\exists x)(fx . \sim gx)$ $\sim$A, $\sim(x)(fx \supset gx)$.

That A and E can be true together is made plain by writing them in the
$\sim$O and $\sim$I forms. The condition for their being jointly true is the falsity
of "$(\exists x)fx$": if there is no f then there is no f which is not g, and also no f
which is g. Thus each of the pair of statements, "No winged horses are
non-herbivorous", "No winged horses are herbivorous", is made true by
the fact that there is no winged horse. In cases in which the conjunction
of an A and an E statement is felt to be unnatural, what undoubtedly
happens is that what is understood but is unexpressed is treated as if it
were stated as part of the conjunction, namely, that $(\exists x)fx$. And if it is
felt to be strange to say "All the Cadillacs in my garage are solid gold
because there are no Cadillacs in my garage", it is because the A statement
is interpreted to mean "There are Cadillacs in my garage and each one
is solid gold", instead of being interpreted to mean "There is nothing in

my garage which is both a Cadillac and is not solid gold". When a disappointed fisherman tells us, "All the barracuda I caught I can put in my vest pocket", we take him not to be making a false statement but to be asserting something which is made true by a deplorable fact.

Some Quantificational Equivalences

Reflection on the set of equivalences above shows that either one of the symbols "(x)", "$(\exists x)$" can be dispensed with. Whatever can be expressed with the help of "(x)" and "$\sim$" can be expressed in terms of "$\sim$" and "$(\exists x)$", and whatever can be expressed with the help of "$(\exists x)$" and "$\sim$" can be expressed in terms of "$\sim$" and "(x)". The set of equivalences below shows this:

$$A, \sim(\exists x)(fx . \sim gx) . \equiv . \quad (x)(fx \supset gx)$$
$$E, \sim(\exists x)(fx . gx) \quad . \equiv . \quad (x)(fx \supset \sim gx)$$
$$I, \quad (\exists x)(fx . gx) \quad . \equiv . \sim(x)(fx \supset \sim gx)$$
$$O, \quad (\exists x)(fx . \sim gx) . \equiv . \sim(x)(fx \supset gx).$$

How "(x)" is to be rewritten in terms of "$(\exists x)$" and "$\sim$" can easily be seen from the equivalence, $A \equiv \sim O$:

$$(x)(fx \supset gx) . \equiv . \sim(\exists x)(fx . \sim gx)$$
$$\equiv . \sim(\exists x) \sim (fx \supset gx) \qquad [\text{i.e.,} \sim(p \supset q) . \equiv . p . \sim q].$$

Hence,

$$F1 \qquad (x)(\quad) . \equiv . \sim(\exists x) \sim (\quad).$$

A pair of statements whose forms involve but one functional variable will make this equivalence immediately obvious:

Everything is material
There does not exist anything which is not material.

How "$(\exists x)$" is to be construed in terms of "(x)" and "$\sim$" is to be seen from the equivalence, $O \equiv \sim A$:

$$(\exists x)(fx . \sim gx) . \equiv . \sim(x)(fx \supset gx)$$
$$\equiv . \sim(x) \sim (fx . \sim gx) \qquad [\text{i.e.,} p \supset q . \equiv . \sim(p . \sim q)].$$

Hence,

$$F2 \qquad (\exists x)(\quad) . \equiv . \sim(x) \sim (\quad).$$

The following pair of statements illustrates this equivalence:

Something is organic
Not everything is nonorganic.

For convenient reference we list equivalences involving a change of quantifier:

$$
\begin{array}{ll}
\text{F1} & (x)fx \ . \ \equiv \ . \sim(\exists x) \sim fx \\
\text{F2} & (\exists x)fx \ . \ \equiv \ . \sim(x) \sim fx \\
\text{F3} & \sim(x)fx \ . \ \equiv \ . \ (\exists x) \sim fx \\
\text{F4} & \sim(\exists x)fx \ . \ \equiv \ . \ (x) \sim fx.
\end{array}
$$

The Diagrammatic Method for Testing Inferences

The above equivalences provide the means for making various inferences from single statement-forms. The validity of these inferences is made perspicuous by the use of diagrams originated by the English logician John Venn (1834–1883). Within overlapping circles the various compartments represent the denotation of "*f* and *g*", "*f* and not *g*", "not *f* and *g*", i.e., all the things which make "$fx \ . \ gx$", "$fx \ . \sim gx$", etc., true when the terms "*f*" and "*g*" are fixed. The fact that a function has no values is represented by shading its compartment in the diagram; its having a value is signified by placing a cross in its compartment; leaving the compartment blank represents its being unknown whether or not the function has values. To illustrate, the diagrammatic representation of

$$\sim(\exists x)(fx \ . \sim gx) \ . \ (\exists x)fx \qquad \text{is}$$

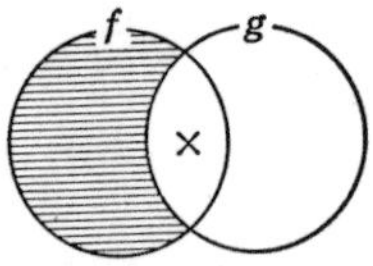

FIGURE 2.

The shaded part of the *f*-circle which lies outside the *g*-circle indicates that there are no values of "$fx \ . \sim gx$", and the cross in the remaining compartment of the *f*-circle indicates that "fx" has values. Inconsistency between two statement-forms, e.g., between "$\sim(\exists x)fx$" and "$(\exists x)fx$", is represented by a section that at the same time is shaded and has a cross. In order, therefore, that an inconsistency not show up on the diagram when none in fact exists, the rule to follow in representing combinations of universal and existential statements is to diagram the universal first. In the example given, "$\sim(\exists x)(fx \ . \sim gx)$" is diagrammed first, then "$(\exists x)fx$", else the cross might appear in a region which the representation of the first statement requires to be shaded.

The fact that one statement-form implies another is shown by the fact that in diagramming the first we automatically diagram the second. This will be illustrated in the diagrams of inferences from the statement-forms considered below. Since a number of the inferences involve nothing more than transformations justified by equivalences between truth-functions [e.g., between "$fx \ . \sim gx$" and "$\sim(\sim gx \supset \sim fx)$"], comment

will be made only in those cases in which from a given statement-form
a further formula having a different quantifier is inferred. The double line
beneath a statement-form indicates that the formulas below it are inferences
from it.

$$\frac{(\exists x)(fx \cdot gx)}{\begin{array}{l}(\exists x)(gx \cdot fx)\\(\exists x)\sim(gx \supset \sim\!fx)\\\sim(x)(fx \supset \sim\!gx)\end{array}}$$

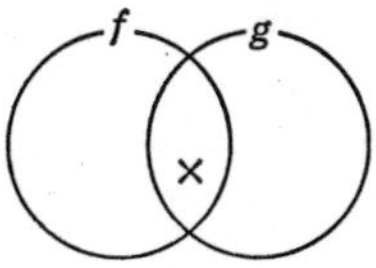

FIGURE 3.

The third conclusion is justified by F2:

$$(\exists x)(fx \cdot gx) \,.\, \equiv \,.\, \sim(x)\sim(fx \cdot gx) \,.\, \equiv \,.\, \sim(x)(fx \supset \sim\!gx).$$

For example, given that there are swans that are black, we may conclude
that not everything is such that if it is a swan it is not black.

$$\frac{(\exists x)(fx \cdot \sim\!gx)}{\begin{array}{l}(\exists x)(\sim\!gx \cdot fx)\\(\exists x)\sim(\sim\!gx \supset \sim\!fx)\\\sim(x)(fx \supset gx)\end{array}}$$

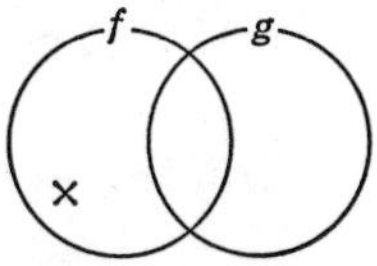

FIGURE 4.

The third conclusion is justified by F2:

$$(\exists x)(fx \cdot \sim\!gx) \,.\, \equiv \,.\, \sim(x)\sim(fx \cdot \sim\!gx) \,.\, \equiv \,.\, \sim(x)(fx \supset gx).$$

For example, given that some dogs are not terriers, we may conclude that
not everything which is a dog is a terrier.

$$\frac{(x)(fx \supset gx)}{\begin{array}{l}(x)(\sim\!gx \supset \sim\!fx)\\\sim(\exists x)(\sim\!gx \cdot fx)\end{array}}$$

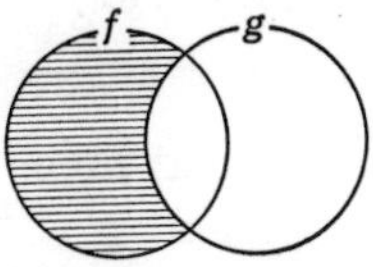

FIGURE 5.

The second conclusion is justified by F1:

$$(x)(fx \supset gx) \,.\, \equiv \,.\, \sim(\exists x)\sim(fx \supset gx) \,.\, \equiv \,.\, \sim(\exists x)(\sim\!gx \cdot fx).$$

For example, given that all men are mortal, we may conclude that there
is nothing which is both immortal and a man.

$$\frac{\sim(\exists x)(fx \cdot gx)}{\begin{array}{l}\sim(\exists x)(gx \cdot fx)\\(x)(gx \supset \sim\!fx)\\(x)(fx \supset \sim\!gx)\end{array}}$$

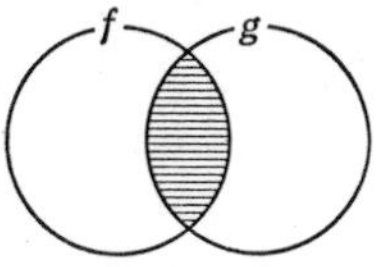

FIGURE 6.

The third conclusion is justified by F4:

$$\sim(\exists x)(fx \cdot gx) \,.\, \equiv \,.\, (x)\sim(fx \cdot gx) \,.\, \equiv \,.\, (x)(fx \supset \sim gx).$$

For example, given that no perfect numbers are odd, we may conclude that all perfect numbers are non-odd.

Diagrams also make obvious the following inferences from a universal generalization conjoined with an existential condition, in these cases from the "composite" A and E to the corresponding I and O:

$$\frac{\begin{array}{l}(x)(fx \supset gx)\\(\exists x)fx\end{array}}{(\exists x)(fx \cdot gx)}$$

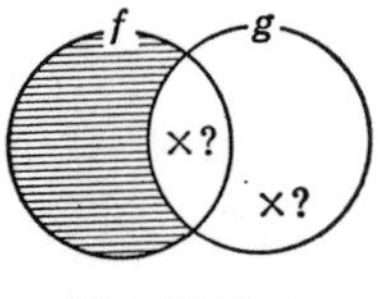

FIGURE 7.

$$\frac{\begin{array}{l}(x)(fx \supset \sim gx)\\(\exists x)fx\end{array}}{(\exists x)(fx \cdot \sim gx)}$$

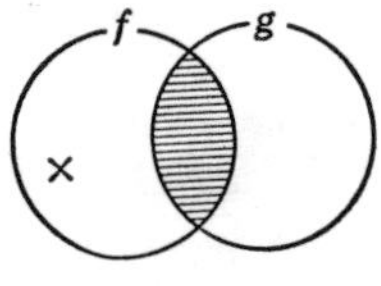

FIGURE 8.

The fact that an inference is invalid is reflected in the fact that diagramming the premises does not at the same time diagram the conclusion:

$$\frac{\begin{array}{l}(x)(fx \supset gx)\\(\exists x)gx\end{array}}{(\exists x)(fx \cdot gx)}$$

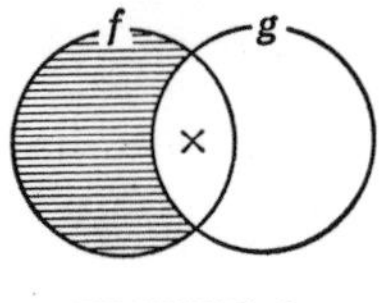

FIGURE 9.

The diagram of the second premise specifies only that one or other of the two compartments "f and g", "not-f and g", has a cross, whereas the diagram of the conclusion specifies a cross in "f and g". The diagram of the conclusion adds something to the diagram of the premises; hence the conclusion cannot be read off from the diagram of the premises. This inference involves a fallacy analogous to that of affirming the consequent of "$p \supset q$" and deducing "p".

Syllogistic Inference

Inferences which consist in passing from a pair of A, E, I, O statements having a term in common to a third statement of one of these kinds as their consequent are called syllogistic. A *syllogism* is defined as an argument constituted of two premises and a conclusion so related to each other as to contain among them exactly three terms, "f", "g", "h", each

51222

term appearing in two of the three statements. The following are examples of syllogistic reasoning, together with the formal schema which each exemplifies:

(a) All logicians are intrigued by symbols $\qquad (x)(gx \supset hx)$
All mathematicians are logicians $\qquad\qquad (x)(fx \supset gx)$

All mathematicians are intrigued by symbols $\quad (x)(fx \supset hx)$

(b) No elephants are agile $\qquad\qquad\qquad \sim(\exists x)(hx \, . \, gx)$
Some agile creatures are carnivorous $\qquad (\exists x)(gx \, . \, fx)$

Some carnivorous creatures are not elephants $\quad (\exists x)(fx \, . \sim hx)$

Both of these are valid pieces of reasoning. The first syllogism has the form which Aristotle designated as perfect, and its validity is obvious. The validity of the second is perhaps not so obvious, and for such arguments rules have been formulated by means of which they can be tested.

The terminology in which medieval logicians framed rules for testing syllogisms leaves much to be desired, presupposing as it does that the A, E, I, O forms of statement are of the subject-predicate kind, and that A and I are affirmative while E and O are negative. For one thing, analysis shows that the two terms "f" and "g" do not differ in their nature. The so-called subject and predicate of an I statement, for example, are both predicate terms, neither characterizing the other but both characterizing an *individual*. For another thing, there is better reason, terminologically, for describing A and E as negative, in that their sole force is to deny existence, and I and O as affirmative, in that they assert existence, than to classify them in the traditional fashion. Furthermore, syllogistic theory was developed to a degree of complication out of proportion to its importance for formal reasoning. Here we shall give the standard six rules without comment, and proceed to formulate a smaller set which lays down the necessary and sufficient conditions for syllogistic validity. An understanding of either set of rules requires an explanation of the notion of distribution.

Distribution of Terms

A term "f" is said to be distributed in a statement if all of its denotation, i.e., all the values of "fx" which make "fx" true, are referred to by the statement; otherwise it is said to be undistributed. Consider again the forms "All f is g", "No f is g", "Some f is g", "Some f is not g". In the I and O statement-forms "f" is clearly undistributed, since not all the things to which "f" applies are referred to. In the A form "f" clearly is distributed. Since E can be equivalently expressed as "All f is non-g", "f" is also distributed in E. The distribution of "g" in the four forms is less obvious. We can argue that it is not distributed in A and I on the ground that if it were then we could validly infer from each "All g is f". For it is plain that if all of a term's denotation is referred to by the given statement, then a statement again referring to all of its denotation is inferrible. However, from "All terriers are dogs" it is not possible validly to infer "All dogs are terriers", nor from "Some men are factory employees" is it possible to infer "All factory employees are men". The following equivalence shows that the I form distributes neither of its terms:

$$(\exists x)(fx \cdot gx) \cdot \equiv \cdot \sim(x)(gx \supset \sim fx).$$

Letting "f" and "g" stand for "man" and "factory employee", the formula on the right of the equivalence reads, "Not all factory employees are non-men". This clearly leaves "factory employees" undistributed. A similar consideration shows both "f" and "g" in the E form to be distributed:

$$\sim(\exists x)(fx \cdot gx) \cdot \equiv \cdot (x)(fx \supset \sim gx) \cdot \equiv \cdot (x)(gx \supset \sim fx).$$

As for the O, in asserting that some f are not g, what is stated is that there is an f which is different from *every* g. Thus O distributes "g". To sum up the patterns of distribution:

D U

All f is g

D   D

No f is g

U U

Some f is g

U   D

Some f is not g.

Syllogistic Rules

The syllogistic rules as traditionally stated are the following:

1. The middle term (the term common to the two premises) must be distributed at least once
2. No term undistributed in the premises may be distributed in the conclusion
3. If both premises are negative (EE, EO, or OO) no conclusion is possible
4. If one premise is negative the conclusion must be negative
5. If neither premise is negative the conclusion must be affirmative (A or I).

To these rules, formulated by medieval logicians, has been added a further rule,

6. If both premises are universal the conclusion cannot be particular (I or O).

The rules we lay down form a set from which the above can be deduced. They are:

(1) The term common to the premises must be distributed exactly once
(2) The distribution of the terms of the conclusion must be exactly as in the premises
(3) At least one of the premises must be universal
(4) The conclusion is particular if and only if one premise is particular.

Examination of syllogisms (a) and (b) above shows that they conform to these four rules. If the conclusion of (a) is replaced by "All people intrigued by symbols are mathematicians", and the conclusion of (b) by "Some elephants are not carnivorous", the new syllogisms violate rule (2) and are invalid.

Diagrammatic Testing

A test for syllogistic validity which is quite independent of the use of rules is provided by Venn diagrams for three terms, represented by three intersecting circles. In addition to being an independent method for testing syllogisms, the diagrammatic technique makes perspicuous what conformity with, or violation of, one of the four rules comes to. By diagramming syllogisms each of which satisfies three of the rules and violates the remaining rule we can illustrate both the rules test and the diagram test. In doing this it is shown also that the rules are *independent*, that is, that no rule is a consequence of any combination of the remaining rules. Independence of a rule R is established by exhibiting a syllogism which violates it while satisfying the other rules, and we shall choose our examples so as to exhibit independence.

The validity of a syllogism is reflected in the diagram by the fact that the representation of the premises contains a possible representation of the conclusion. This is to say that the conclusion of a valid syllogism can be read off from the representation of the premises. Observing the rule of diagramming the universal premise first, the following syllogism is seen to conform to all four rules:

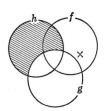

All Algerians are religious $\qquad (x)(hx \supset gx)$
Some Frenchmen are not religious $\qquad (\exists x)(fx . \sim gx)$
_____
Some Frenchmen are not Algerians $\qquad (\exists x)(fx . \sim hx)$

FIGURE 10.

Each of the syllogisms below is invalid, and violates one, and only one, of the four rules. The number of the syllogism will be the number of the rule it violates.

(1) No politicians are incorruptible $\sim(\exists x)(hx \cdot gx)$
No bankers are incorruptible $\sim(\exists x)(fx \cdot gx)$
────────────────────────
No bankers are politicians $\sim(\exists x)(fx \cdot hx)$

FIGURE 11.

It will be observed that the region common to "*f*" and "*h*" is not shaded, as the conclusion requires. All rules except the first, which requires that the common term be distributed but once, are satisfied.

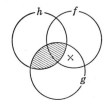

(2) No pygmies are educated $\sim(\exists x)(gx \cdot hx)$
Some pygmies are warriors $(\exists x)(gx \cdot fx)$
────────────────────────
Some warriors are educated $(\exists x)(fx \cdot hx)$

FIGURE 12.

If the syllogisms were valid the diagram of the premises would show a cross in the section common to "*f*" and "*h*". It is clear that "Some *f* are not *h*" is a validly derivable conclusion.

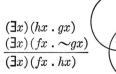
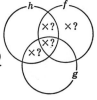

(3) Some night prowlers are lions $(\exists x)(hx \cdot gx)$
Some carnivores are not lions $(\exists x)(fx \cdot \sim gx)$
────────────────────────
Some carnivores are night prowlers $(\exists x)(fx \cdot hx)$

FIGURE 13.

The diagram of the first premise specifies a cross in either the section common to "*h*", "*g*", and "*f*" or the section common to "*h*", "*g*", and "not-*f*", while the diagram of the second premise specifies a cross in either the "*f*, not-*g*, *h*" compartment or the "*f*, not-*g*, not-*h*" compartment. The diagram of their conjunction therefore does not specify that there be a cross in either the "*f, h,* not-*g*" compartment or the "*f, h, g*" compartment, which the diagram of the conclusion does specify.

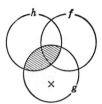

(4)	No boxers are old	$\sim(\exists x)(gx \cdot hx)$
	Some boxers are not successful	$(\exists x)(gx \cdot \sim fx)$
	No successful people are old	$\sim(\exists x)(fx \cdot hx)$

FIGURE 14.

It should be pointed out that the set (1) through (4) eliminates two combinations which the traditional set of rules, without 6, allows, namely, EAO and AAI. Rules (1) and (2) together eliminate all the EAO and AAI combinations. Let us see how they effect this for AAI combinations.

(a)	$(x)(gx \supset hx)$	(b)	$(x)(gx \supset hx)$
	$(x)(fx \supset gx)$		$(x)(gx \supset fx)$
	$(\exists x)(fx \cdot hx)$		$(\exists x)(fx \cdot hx)$

(c)	$(x)(hx \supset gx)$	(d)	$(x)(hx \supset gx)$
	$(x)(gx \supset fx)$		$(x)(fx \supset gx)$
	$(\exists x)(fx \cdot hx)$		$(\exists x)(fx \cdot hx)$

Classical logicians considered the first three of these valid because they took all terms to have a denotation: an A statement was treated as a "composite" A, or a conjunction of a universal affirmative with an existential condition. On the present interpretation of A and E as "$\sim(\exists x)(fx \cdot \sim gx)$" and "$\sim(\exists x)(fx \cdot gx)$", it is clear that no existential statement may be inferred from any AA or AE premises. But by adjoining to the given set of premises appropriate existence assertions, the conclusions become valid, as diagrams show. Thus, by conjoining "$(\exists x)fx$" to the premises of (a) the conclusion can be seen to follow:

$$\frac{(x)(gx \supset hx) \cdot (x)(fx \supset gx)}{(\exists x)fx} \quad .$$
$$\overline{(\exists x)(fx \cdot hx)}$$

Similarly, conjoining "$(\exists x)gx$" with the premises of (b), and "$(\exists x)hx$" with the premises of (c), yields the given conclusion. Reinforcing a syllogism in this way has, in case (b), the effect of turning a syllogism the premises of which violate the distributive rule for the common term into a valid argument. If, for example, to the premises "All statesmen are incorruptible" and "All statesmen are wise" we add the statement

"There are statesmen", we may validly infer "Some wise people are incorruptible".

Non-syllogistic Inference

In addition to the syllogism there are further forms of inference that hinge on the concepts developed in the preceding sections of Part II. Consider the following argument:

> All wild azaleas are easy to grow but not easy to transplant
> Some things are easily transplanted
> ──
> There are things which are either not wild or not azaleas

Its form is given by

$$(x)(fx . gx . \supset . hx . {\sim}jx) . (\exists x)jx . \supset . (\exists x)({\sim}fx \lor {\sim}gx).$$

If we examine the following simple inferences in which, unlike the syllogism, one premise quantifies only one of the occurrences of the individual variable falling within the scope of the quantifier in the other premise, we shall be able to discover the form of which it is a special case. The following are a sample of such simple inferences. All of them may be tested for validity by the use of diagrams (diagramming, as usual, the non-existential form first).

(a) $(x)(fx \supset gx)$
$(\exists x)fx$
─────────
$(\exists x)gx$,

(b) $(x)(fx \supset gx)$
${\sim}(\exists x)gx$
─────────
${\sim}(\exists x)fx$,

(c) $(x)(fx \supset gx)$
$(\exists x){\sim}gx$
─────────
${\sim}(x)fx, (\exists x){\sim}fx$,

(d) $(\exists x)(fx \lor gx)$
${\sim}(\exists x)fx$
─────────
$(\exists x)gx$,

(e) $(x)(fx . gx)$
$(\exists x)fx$
─────────
$(\exists x)gx$,

(f) $(x)(fx \supset gx)$
$(x)fx$
─────────
$(x)gx$.

The example above is seen to be a special case of (c). The universal premise is a generalization on a function with a complex antecendent and consequent, and the existential premise is a generalization on a function which implies the falsity of that consequent. In effect, to say that the example is a special case of (c) is to refer in an indirect way to the fact that in any valid inference-schema the substitution of unquantified functions for "fx" and "gx" will yield a valid result.

The diagram of (c) shows that "$(\exists x){\sim}fx$" is a valid conclusion, but that "${\sim}(\exists x)fx$" is not. It is instructive to note some further examples of invalid inference. In some cases the invalidity of the inference is obvious at a glance because of its analogy to an invalid truth-functional schema; in other cases it revolves on an understanding of the import of operators.

And in all cases, of course, diagramming the premises provides a simple answer to questions of validity. The following are all invalid:

(α) $\dfrac{\begin{array}{l}(x)(fx \supset gx)\\ \sim(\exists x)fx\end{array}}{\sim(\exists x)gx}$,

(β) $\dfrac{\begin{array}{l}(x)(fx \supset gx)\\ (\exists x)\sim fx\end{array}}{(\exists x)\sim gx}$,

(γ) $\dfrac{\begin{array}{l}(x)(fx \supset gx)\\ (\exists x)gx\end{array}}{(\exists x)fx}$,

(δ) $\dfrac{\begin{array}{l}(\exists x)(fx \vee gx)\\ (\exists x)\sim fx\end{array}}{(\exists x)gx}$,

(ϵ) $\dfrac{\begin{array}{l}(\exists x)(fx \supset gx)\\ (\exists x)fx\end{array}}{(\exists x)gx}$.

Example (δ) is most conveniently represented by using straight lines to diagram the denotation of the functions "$fx \vee gx$" and "$\sim fx$". A line spanning two or more compartments will indicate that the function whose denotation is represented by the compartments has a value, lying in one or other of the spanned sections. Thus the diagram for the three statement-forms is

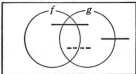

FIGURE 15.

The first premise is made true by having a value lying in any one of the three compartments spanned by the uppermost of the two lines, that is, in any one of the sections common to "f" and "not-g", "f" and "g", or "g" and "not-f". The second premise is made true by having a value lying in either of the compartments spanned by the middle line, that is, in one of the sections common to "not-f" and "g" or "not-f" and "not-g". The representation of the conclusion requires a line spanning the compartments common to "g" and "f", and "g" and "not-f", since the conclusion is made true by a value lying in one or other compartment of the g-circle. The conclusion, represented by the broken line, adds something to the diagram of the premises and cannot be read off from it. Hence the conclusion is not validly inferrible.

With the above groups of simple valid and invalid schemata at hand it is possible easily to determine the validity of the following more complex forms of inference:

$\dfrac{\begin{array}{l}(x)(fx \,.\, \supset .\, gx \supset hx)\\ (\exists x)(gx \,.\, \sim hx)\end{array}}{\sim(\exists x)fx}$,

$\dfrac{\begin{array}{l}(x)(fx \vee gx \,.\, \supset .\, hx)\\ \sim(\exists x)hx\end{array}}{(x)\sim(\sim fx \supset gx)}$,

$\dfrac{\begin{array}{l}(x)(fx \,.\, \supset .\, \sim gx \supset hx)\\ (x)(gx \,.\, \supset .\, kx \,.\, lx)\end{array}}{(x)(fx \,.\, \sim hx \,.\, \supset .\, lx)}$.

HINT: the functions generalized in the premises of the third example may be transformed in accordance with the truth-function equivalence "$p . \supset . q \supset r : \equiv : p . \sim r . \supset . \sim q$", and the conclusion derived from the transformed premises in accordance with the principle "$p \supset q . q \supset r . \supset . p \supset r$".

An examination of the valid forms (**a**) through (**f**), together with the general principle that $A . B . \supset . C$ is equivalent to $A . \supset . B \supset C$, reveals interesting possibilities of distributing quantifiers throughout a statement-form, and suggests others. Using the principle to transform (**a**), "$(x)(fx \supset gx) . (\exists x)fx . \supset . (\exists x)gx$", into

$$(\mathbf{a'}) \quad (x)(fx \supset gx) . \supset : (\exists x)fx . \supset . (\exists x)gx,$$

quantifiers having relatively restricted scope are distributed throughout the formula "$fx \supset gx$". Similarly, (**f**) when so transformed yields

$$(\mathbf{f'}) \quad (x)(fx \supset gx) . \supset : (x)fx . \supset . (x)gx.$$

The character of these statement-forms is analogous to that of a tautology: the implications hold for all values of the (free) functional variables. The difference is that we can no longer use anything so simple as a truth-table to exhibit their validity.

It is to be remarked that with regard to neither (**a'**) nor (**f'**) does the converse implication hold. This is perhaps obvious in the case of (**a'**). It is made clear in the case of (**f'**) by the consideration that a statement of the form "$\sim(x)fx$" makes "$(x)fx . \supset . (x)gx$" true while leaving the truth-value of "$(x)(fx \supset gx)$" undetermined. Another example of an implication which holds without its converse being true is

$$(\exists x)(fx . gx) . \supset : (\exists x)fx . (\exists x)gx.$$

The consequent is made true if there are two things, one having the property f and the other the property g, whereas the former requires the existence of something having both properties. Formulas within each of the following pairs, however, are equivalent: "$(\exists x)(fx \lor gx)$" and "$(\exists x)fx \lor (\exists x)gx$", "$(x)(fx . gx)$" and "$(x)fx . (x)gx$". The set of inference rules for distributing quantifiers is given here for convenient reference:

F5	$(x)(fx \supset gx) . \supset : (\exists x)fx . \supset . (\exists x)gx$
F6	$(x)(fx \supset gx) . \supset : (x)fx . \supset . (x)gx$
F7	$(\exists x)(fx . gx) . \supset : (\exists x)fx . (\exists x)gx$
F8	$(\exists x)(fx \lor gx) . \equiv : (\exists x)fx . \lor . (\exists x)gx$
F9	$(x)(fx . gx) . \equiv : (x)fx . (x)gx$.

Formation Rules

So far we have proceeded informally in our exposition of valid inferences involving quantified statement-forms, without any attempt at doing what is requisite for ordering the material in a deductive system. In order to construct a system for the deduction of valid quantified formulas we should need to state explicitly the syntax of the extension of language ushered in by individual variables, functional variables, and quantification symbols, and lay down the axioms from which these formulas are derived. Such an undertaking lies beyond the limits of the present work. However, we shall give an account of the formation rules operative in one such system, the so-called *functional calculus of first order*, so as to introduce the reader to forms not so far considered. Among these are functions of more than one argument, such as "$f(x,y)$", "$f(x,y,z)$", examples of which are "x is next to y", "x gives y to z". The functional calculus of first order, which quantifies only individual variables, contains the propositional calculus as a part, so that the formation rules of the latter are included among its rules. It has in addition the following:

> If c is a functional variable of n arguments and if $a_1, a_2, \ldots, a_n$ are individual variables, then $c(a_1, a_2, \ldots, a_n)$ is wellformed
> If A is wellformed and a is an individual variable (a)A is wellformed.

It is plain from these rules that "fx", "$(x)fx$", "$f(x,y)$", "$(x)[(\exists y)f(x,y)]$" are all wellformed formulas (the existential quantifier being definitionally introduced). But in addition to these, as the rules indicate, the following count as wellformed:

$$(x)p, \qquad (\exists x)p, \qquad (x)(p \supset fx).$$

It might seem odd to include such expressions as these when "p" does not contain the variable "x". For it is natural to suppose that a quantifier can have in its scope only components which refer back to it, i.e., only components containing a variable duplicating that inside the quantifier symbol. Actually, however, it is of some importance, in manipulating quantified expressions, to be able to shift the scope of a quantifier to include such components. And it is also useful to be able to do this when expressing the forms of some statements of ordinary discourse. To illustrate, consider the two pairs of equivalents,

> Someone is such that if the authorities enact a new law he will be fined*
> If the authorities enact a new law someone will be fined,

and

> Everyone is such that if the game is lost he loses money*
> If the game is lost everyone loses money.

The first member of each pair of equivalents is a generalization having within its scope a statement whose form is "p", where "p" contains no individual variable associated with the quantification symbol. In the second member of each pair that statement is removed from the scope of

---

* The meaning here is clear although expressed in unidiomatic English.

the generalization. Equivalence of form between the paired statements is expressed in the *confinement formulas*

$$\text{F10} \qquad (\exists x)(p \supset fx) . \equiv : p . \supset . (\exists x)fx$$
$$\text{F11} \qquad (x)(p \supset fx) . \equiv : p . \supset . (x)fx,$$

where "p" is understood to contain no free occurrences of "x". Somewhat more surprising equivalences are

$$\text{F12} \qquad (x)(fx \supset p) . \equiv : (\exists x)fx . \supset . p$$
$$\text{F13} \qquad (\exists x)(fx \supset p) . \equiv : (x)fx . \supset . p.$$

An instance of F12 is the pair of statements

> Everyone is such that if he tips off the police, the narcotics ring will be broken up
> If someone tips off the police, then the narcotics ring will be broken up.

Other useful equivalences in which a shift in the scope of the quantifier occurs are

$$\text{F14} \qquad (\exists x)(fx . p) . \equiv . p . (\exists x)fx$$
$$\text{F15} \qquad (x)(fx . p) . \equiv . (x)fx . p.$$

N-placed Predicates

Functions involving more than one argument, symbolized by "$f(x,y)$", "$f(x,y,z)$", etc., are essential for exhibiting the forms of many statements whose logical connections with each other we wish to set out. Monadic functions "fx", "gy", etc., i.e., functions of a single argument, turn out to be inadequate for exhibiting the logical structure common to "6 is greater than 5", and "10 is less than 13", and to "4 is between 3 and 8" and "point a is between points b and c", and also for distinguishing these pairs from each other. These statements involve what are called *relative terms*, and are structurally more complex than the sort of statements we have studied up to the present. Their analysis brings to light functions of more than one argument. Investigation of these functions and of the statement-forms resulting from quantification of the individual variables in them will enable us to justify forms of inference which otherwise we could not. For example, consider the logically connected statements

> Every man has a father
> Every man has one and the same father.

Inspection shows that from the second the first can be inferred, but that the second cannot validly be inferred from the first. If we are confined to the notation developed so far, the form of the first will be represented by

"$(x)(fx \supset gx)$" and the form of the second by "$(x)(fx \supset hx)$", where "gx" is interpreted as "x has a father" and "hx" as "x has one and the same father". Neither the validity of the one inference nor the invalidity of the other is apparent from this way of writing them. The case is similar with regard to the pair of statements "All squares are rectangles" and "The diagonal of a square is the diagonal of a rectangle". If these statements have their forms represented respectively by "$(x)(fx \supset gx)$" and "$(x)(hx \supset jx)$", no connection between them is visible nor is there any suggestion that the second can be inferred from the first.

In order to make the validity of such inferences apparent, some sort of formal distinctions must be made between the statements figuring in them. And within the quantified statements a distinction must be made between the kinds of function quantified. The possibility of quantified expressions themselves falling within the scope of a quantifier is already present in such a formula as "$(x)(p \supset fx)$". Replacing "p" by "$(\exists y)gy$" to obtain "$(x)[(\exists y)gy \cdot \supset \cdot fx]$" we have the form of the statement "Everyone is such that if there are terrorists he is frightened". Here the two quantifiers bind the variables of two monadic functions. It is often the case, however, that what is requisite to exhibit the form of a statement is a formula all of whose quantifiers operate on the variables of a single function of several arguments. The formation rules permit as wellformed such an expression as "$(x)[(\exists y)f(x,y)]$", which differs from the form of the above example in the type of function to which the quantifiers refer. Without the possibility of framing such formulas we should be without the means of expressing the forms of the many logically complex statements which occur in mathematics, e.g., the definition of a continuous function. We have now to consider these more complex formulas.

It is natural to think of "fx", "gy", etc., as the forms of statements which grammatically are subject-predicate, e.g., "Jones is miserly". The name *one-place predicate* is sometimes given the predicate occurring in such a form as "x is miserly". By freeing one's mind of grammatical considerations one can interpret "predicate" in an extended sense to cover what is asserted of "x" in such an expression as "x will visit the mother of x unless the vacation of x is canceled". It is but a short step to extending the notion of a predicate to what is asserted of a number of terms taken all together or in subgroups, as in "If x blackballs y then z will sever relations with x". Such an expression can be regarded as the form of a statement containing a *several-placed predicate*, or *relational predicate*, and two or more names. On freeing it and similar forms of their non-formal terms we have the formulas "$f(x,y)$", "$f(x,y,z)$", etc., denoting functions of more than one argument—dyadic, triadic, . . ., n-adic functions. With these at hand, we can explicitly distinguish the respects in which the following differ formally from each other: "White sits between Jones and Smith",

"Jones is Smith's worst enemy", "Jones is his own worst enemy", "White is thrifty". The first statement is an instance of "$h(z,x,y)$", the second of "$f(x,y)$", the third of "$f(x,x)$", and the last of "gz". The notational distinctions between "$f(x,y)$" and "$f(y,x)$" and between "$h(x,y,z)$" and "$h(z,x,y)$" reflect the difference in what is called the "sense" of the relation. The dyadic functions "x is enemy of y" and "y is enemy of x" are distinguished notationally by the reversal of "x" and "y" in the first pair of formulas above, and "x is between y and z" and "z is between x and y" are distinguished by the order of the variables in the second pair.

It is possible from here to proceed in our analysis beyond statement-forms such as "$(x)[\exists y)gy . \supset . fx]$" and "$(\exists x)fx . \supset . (\exists x)gx$", to statement-forms which are like these in involving more than one element of generality but different from them in quantifying each of the variables of an n-adic function. The following are some of the statement-forms which can be constructed, and whose relations to each other need to be examined:

$$(x)(y)f(x,y) \qquad (\exists x)(\exists y)f(x,y)$$
$$(y)(x)f(x,y), \qquad (\exists y)(\exists x)f(x,y),$$

$$(x)(\exists y)f(x,y) \qquad \sim(x)(\exists y)f(x,y) \qquad (x)(\exists y)(z)f(x,y,z)$$
$$(\exists y)(x)f(x,y) \qquad (x)\sim(\exists y)f(x,y) \qquad (\exists x)(y)(z)f(x,y,z)$$
$$(x)(\exists y)f(y,x), \qquad (\exists x)(y)f(x,y), \qquad (\exists x)(y)(\exists z)f(x,y,z).$$

The conventions with regard to the scope of the quantifiers in such multi-quantified formulas are: (1) the quantifier in the outermost position has the widest scope; (2) the scope of each succeeding quantifier extends past the expression succeeding it.

It has already been seen how changing the distribution of quantifiers can affect the import of a quantified expression. The formula "$(\exists x)(fx . gx)$" means something different from "$(\exists x)fx . (\exists x)gx$", the first implying the second, but not conversely. A shift in the scope of a quantifier often results in a formula which neither implies nor is implied by the original. Hence in order to determine the implication relations between various quantified statement-forms, it is necessary to observe carefully the scopes of their quantifiers. If an adequate set of postulates for the functional calculus had been given here, the valid formulas we have selected for study would all be provable in the system. In default of proceeding axiomatically we shall illustrate the statement-forms occurring in several valid implications or equivalences, with the aim of making the implications or equivalences intuitively obvious.

Consider the statement "All war against all", and the equivalence

$$(x)(y)f(x,y) . \equiv . (y)(x)f(x,y).$$

Each of the equivalent formulas gives equally its form. The first says that for each thing x, no matter what y is chosen, x wars against y; and the second, that for each thing y, no matter what x is chosen, x wars against y. The following consideration makes their synonymy evident. The assumption that the universe contains a finite number of things, say a, b, c, together with the universally quantified statement-form "$(x)fx$", implies the conjunction "$fa . fb . fc$". The same assumption together with the existentially quantified statement-form "$(\exists x)fx$" implies the disjunction "$fa \vee fb \vee fc$". Hence conjoining this assumption to "$(x)(y)f(x,y)$" yields the expansion

$$(y)f(a,y) . (y)f(b,y) . (y)f(c,y),$$

which in turn expands into

$$f(a,a) . f(a,b) . f(a,c) : f(b,a) . f(b,b) . f(b,c) : f(c,a) . f(c,b) . f(c,c).$$

It is clear that "$(y)(x)f(x,y)$" would have the same expansion and hence is equivalent to the original.

The same sort of consideration will show that

$$(\exists x)(\exists y)f(x,y) . \equiv . (\exists y)(\exists x)f(x,y),$$

each equivalent serving equally to give the form of "someone loves someone". Both members of the equivalence can be expanded into the same disjunction, as disjunction, like conjunction, is associative and commutative.

More interesting questions concerning the relation of quantified formulas to each other arise when the formulas involve more than one type of quantifier, the same in each but different in scope. It will be useful to elucidate the formal differences between the statements of the following list, some of which are differences in the scopes of different quantifiers.

(1) Every man is husband of every woman
(2) Some man is husband of some woman
(3) Every man is husband of some woman
(4) Some woman has every man as husband
(5) Every woman has some man as husband
(6) Some man is husband of every woman
(7) No man is husband of any woman
(8) No man is husband of every woman
(9) Some man is husband of every woman who has a child.

In order to simplify comparison of these statements with respect to form, we shall for the moment understand the field of variation of "x" to be men and of "y" to be women. With this simplification, and letting "$f(x,y)$" stand for "x is husband of y", the forms of the first two are

(1) $(x)(y)f(x,y),$ (2) $(\exists x)(\exists y)f(x,y).$

It should be noted in passing that F1 and F2 give us the possibility of rewriting (1) as

$$\sim(\exists x)\sim(y)f(x,y)$$

and also as

$$\sim(\exists x)(\exists y)\sim f(x,y),$$

and of rewriting (2) as

$$\sim(x)\sim(\exists y)f(x,y)$$

and also as

$$\sim(x)(y)\sim f(x,y).$$

The first expressions of these two pairs have, respectively, the readings

> There is no man such that not every woman has him as husband
> Not every man is such that there is no woman whose husband he is.

Consider now the two pairs of statements (3), (4), and (5), (6). The formulas corresponding to the first pair are

$$(3) \ \ (x)(\exists y)f(x,y), \qquad (4) \ \ (\exists y)(x)f(x,y),$$

and the formulas corresponding to the second pair are

$$(5) \ \ (y)(\exists x)f(x,y), \qquad (6) \ \ (\exists x)(y)f(x,y).$$

Between the members of these pairs the same relation obtains, so it will suffice to point out the relation in one pair only. Statement (3) is to the effect that for each chosen man x there is a woman y such that x is husband of y. Different choices of x may be associated with different choices of y. That is, when the existential quantifier lies within the scope of a universal quantifier it has the force of "some one or other, not necessarily the same one". Statement (4), on the other hand, asserts that some fixed woman y is such that every x is her husband. Thus, when the existential quantifier has a universal quantifier within its scope, it has the force of "some one and the same". It is obvious that (3) is a consequence of (4): If some one woman has every man as husband, then every man is husband to some woman or other. But the converse does not hold. What is implied by the conjunction of the assumption that the universe consists of a limited number of men a, b, c, and of women d, e, with (3) and also with (4) will exhibit clearly their relation. "$(x)(\exists y)f(x,y)$" expands into

$$(\exists y)f(a,y) \,.\, (\exists y)f(b,y) \,.\, (\exists y)f(c,y),$$

and this in turn becomes

$$\text{I} \qquad f(a,d) \vee f(a,e) \,.\, f(b,d) \vee f(b,e) \,.\, f(c,d) \vee f(c,e).$$

And formula "$(\exists y)(x)f(x,y)$" first becomes

$$(x)f(x,d) \vee (x)f(x,e),$$

and this expands into

II $f(a,d) \cdot f(b,d) \cdot f(c,d) \cdot \vee \cdot f(a,e) \cdot f(b,e) \cdot f(c,e).$

Every condition making the disjunction II true makes I true. But I is made true by "$f(a,e) \cdot f(b,d) \cdot f(c,e)$", which is insufficient to make II true. Thus, although (4) implies (3), (3) does not imply (4). This means that different quantifiers cannot be shifted within a formula to yield an equivalent formula.

The forms of (7) and (8), which are the contradictories of (2) and (6), are

(7) $\sim(\exists x)(\exists y)f(x,y),$ (8) $\sim(\exists x)(y)f(x,y).$

The scope of "$\sim$" in each of these is the entire formula, and each differs in import from an expression in which the negation is shifted inward to the function, e.g., the difference between (7) and the formula "$(\exists x)(\exists y)\sim f(x,y)$" is that the latter is the form of "Some man is such that there is a woman to whom he is not husband". And this, in fact, is the contradictory of (1), "Every man is husband of every women".

Inasmuch as there are equivalent ways of expressing a given quantified formula, it is not always apparent that two formulas are contradictories. There is a simple rule of thumb for finding the contradictory of a given formula, namely, *replace each universal quantifier by an existential quantifier, each existential quantifier by a universal quantifier, and negate the function which all the quantifiers preface.* This, to be sure, requires that all distinct quantifiers either stand at the beginning of a formula or be immediately preceded only by other quantifiers or by negation signs. Formulas (3) and (4), whose quantifiers are so placed, have the following contradictories, derived in accordance with this rule:

(3′) $(\exists x)(y)\sim f(x,y),$ (4′) $(y)(\exists x)\sim f(x,y).$

These, in order, have the readings: "Some man is such that in the case of every woman he is not her husband", "For every woman there is a man who is not her husband". The correctness of the rule of thumb is evident on transforming the negations of (3) and (4) in accordance with F3 and F4:

(3′) $\sim(x)(\exists y)f(x,y) \cdot \equiv \cdot (\exists x)\sim(\exists y)f(x,y) \cdot \equiv \cdot (\exists x)(y)\sim f(x,y)$

(4′) $\sim(\exists y)(x)f(x,y) \cdot \equiv \cdot (y)\sim(x)f(x,y) \cdot \equiv \cdot (y)(\exists x)\sim f(x,y).$

The rewriting of quantified statement-forms in such a way that all of their quantifiers, in uninterrupted array, preface an n-adic formula A containing no quantifiers needs to be considered next. Statement (9), "Some man is husband of every woman who has a child", lends itself to a simple analysis. This asserts that

$(\exists x)[x$ is a man $\cdot (y)(y$ is a woman $\cdot \supset \cdot$
$(\exists z)(z$ is child of $y \supset x$ is husband of $y))].$

In order to come out with all its quantifiers in such an array we first make use of a variant of F15,

$$(y)(fy \cdot p) \cdot \equiv \cdot p \cdot (y)fy,$$

to place "x is a man", in which "y" does not occur free, within the scope of "(y)". We thus obtain

$(\exists x)(y)[x$ is a man $. (y$ is a woman $. \supset .$

$\qquad\qquad (\exists z)(z$ is a child of $y \supset x$ is husband of $y))]$.

A variant on F10,

$$(\exists z)(p \supset fz) \cdot \equiv \cdot p \supset (\exists z)fz,$$

allows us to place "y is a woman", in which "z" does not occur free, within the scope of "$(\exists z)$", and we obtain

$(\exists x)(y)[x$ is a man $. (\exists z)(y$ is a woman $. \supset .$

$\qquad\qquad z$ is child of $y \supset x$ is husband of $y)]$.

Again, by use of a variant on F14,

$$(\exists z)(fz \cdot p) \cdot \equiv \cdot p \cdot (\exists z)fz,$$

"x is a man" is placed within the scope of "$(\exists z)$", with the result

$(\exists x)(y)(\exists z)[x$ is a man $. (y$ is a woman $. \supset .$

$\qquad\qquad z$ is child of $y \supset x$ is husband of $y)]$.

The italicized part, which is of the form $A . \supset . B \supset C$, is equivalently given in the form $A . B . \supset . C$. Using this equivalence, and letting "mx" stand for "x is a man", "wy" for "y is a woman", "$g(z,y)$" for "z is child of y", and "$f(x,y)$" for "x is husband of y", the form of the whole can be set out as

$$(\exists x)(y)(\exists z)[mx : wy \cdot g(z,y) \cdot \supset \cdot f(x,y)].$$

The validity of the more complex of the two inferences with which Part II was introduced can readily be justified with the help of the present logical material, the inference, namely, from "Some even numbers are less than every number greater than the smallest odd prime" to "It is not the case that for every even number x there is a number which is greater than the smallest odd prime and is not greater than x". Letting "ex" stand for "x is an even number", and "$y > a$" for "y is a number greater than the smallest odd prime", the form of the first can be expressed as

$$(\exists x)[ex . (y)(y > a . \supset . x < y)],$$

or as

$$(\exists x)(y)[ex . (y > a . \supset . x < y)].$$

The form of the second is

$$\sim(x)(\exists y)[ex . \supset . y > a . \sim(x < y)].$$

Transformation of the first by F1 and F2 yields the second as its equivalent. Hence the validity of inferring one from the other is assured.

Definite Descriptions

Before leaving the topic of multiply quantified formulas, something should be said of the forms of statements involving phrases which are similar to yet different from proper names, phrases called *definite descriptions*. A definite description is an expression of the form "the so-and-so", for example, "the discoverer of quaternions", "the even prime". The convention in logic is to write "(ιx)" for "the object such that", so that these examples become

$(\iota x)(x$ is discoverer of quaternions), $\quad (\iota x)(x$ is even . x is prime).

It is of considerable importance to be able to explicate the form of statements in which definite descriptions occur as grammatical subjects, statements such as "The prime number greater than 12 and less than 17 is unlucky", "The discoverer of quaternions was Irish". These have the form "the object having f has g", written "$g\{(\iota x)fx\}$". We leave aside the question here as to whether ordinary proper names such as "Socrates", "Eisenhower", "Pegasus" are in fact definite descriptions, and turn to a brief analysis of statements explicitly involving definite descriptions. To give the form of these it is necessary to introduce the notion of *identity*. This notion cannot be formalized in the functional calculus of first order, since it involves quantification of a functional variable, and only individual variables are quantified there. The usual definition of identity is

$$x = y = \text{Df. } (f)(fx \equiv fy).$$

That is, x is said to be identical with y when x and y have all their properties in common.

To make explicit the distinction between "a so-and-so" and "the so-and-so", as these phrases occur in the expressions "an object having f has g" and "the object having f has g", it is required to distinguish between the two existential statement-forms

There is an x such that fx and gx
There is one and only one x such that fx and gx.

The second differs from the first in asserting the uniqueness of the object to which f and g are attributed, i.e., in asserting that at least one and at most one object having f has g. The restriction of the function "$fx . gx$" to just one value is expressed with the help of "$=$". How this term enters into the analysis of the statement "The prime number greater than 12 and less than 17 is unlucky" can be seen from rewriting it as

$$(\exists x)[x \text{ is prime} \,.\, 12 < x < 17 \,.\, (y)(y \text{ is prime} \,.\, 12 < y < 17 \,.\, \equiv \,.\, y = x) \,.$$
$$x \text{ is unlucky}].$$

That is, "There is one and only one prime number x, $12 < x < 17$, and x is unlucky" expands, when all its formal terms are made explicit, into "There is a prime number x greater than 12 and less than 17 which is such that for every number y, y is a prime number greater than 12 and less than 17 if and only if y is identical with x, and x is unlucky". By letting "fx" stand for "x is prime $.\, 12 < x < 17$", and "gx" for "x is unlucky", its form can be seen to be

$$(\exists x)(y)(fx : fy \,.\, \equiv \,.\, y = x : gx).$$

It will be clear that no such statement-form can be inferred from "$(\exists x)(fx \,.\, gx)$", but that the converse implication does hold. The introduction of identity enables us to make explicit forms of inference which cannot be justified by formulas quantifying individual variables only. The properties of "$=$" are formalized in the so-called *calculus of equality*, in which such valid inference schemata as the following are deduced:

$$(x)(y)(fx \,.\, x = y \,.\, \supset \,.\, fy)$$
$$x = z \,.\, y = z \,.\, \supset \,.\, x = y.$$

EXERCISES

1. Give the forms of the following, using quantifiers, variables, and the operators "$\sim$", "$\supset$", etc.

(a) If all sages have beards, then no sages are unbearded.

(b) If only diligent students pass, then no students who are not diligent pass.

(c) If there are no unicorns, no unicorns are gentle.

(d) Someone is such that if he falters, everyone loses courage.

(e) St. Francis loves all anima s.

(f) All who love St. Francis love every animal.

(g) Every person who is either thrifty or prudent will, if he has money, refrain from speculating on the stock market.

(h) If all doctors are benefactors, then if there are doctors, there are benefactors.

(i) There is some point or other between any two points on a line.

(j) There is some one and the same point between every pair of points.

(k) Someone criticizes everybody to someone.

(l) Everybody criticizes someone to somebody.

(m) Somebody criticizes somebody to everyone.

2. Write the negatives of the above in such a way that no negation sign prefaces a quantifier.

3. Test the following syllogisms by the rules and by means of diagrams. Where more than one conclusion is given, state which, if either, is valid.

(a) Some modern music is dissonant. No dissonant music is pleasing to the ear. Hence some modern music is not pleasing to the ear.

(b) Some congressmen are not fine orators. Some fine orators are lovers of classical music. Hence some congressmen are not lovers of classical music.

(c) No lawyer is shy. All shy people are nervous. Therefore, (1) no nervous person is a lawyer, (2) some lawyers are not nervous.

(d) Some speakers are entertaining. Anyone who is a speaker is exhibitionistic. Hence, (1) some entertaining people are exhibitionistic, (2) some exhibitionistic people are not entertaining.

(e) Not all senators are law-abiding. Law-abiding people are never apprehensive. Hence, (1) some senators are apprehensive, (2) some apprehensive people are not senators.

4. (a) Given: 1. Anyone who plays roulette will, if he bets heavily, lose a lot of money and be unhappy
   2. Everyone plays roulette
   3. Someone is not unhappy.
   Question: Does everyone bet heavily?

(b) Given: 1. There is no one in the smart set who reads widely or keeps up on current affairs
   2. Everyone with incomes above $10,000 is in the smart set
   3. If anyone fails to keep up on current affairs he should not vote.
   Question: Are there people with incomes above $10,000 who should not vote?

5. Write the following so that all quantifiers stand in uninterrupted array before the function quantified. Find the contradictory of each result in terms of different quantifiers.
   (a) Some one number is less than all numbers greater than 1.
   (b) Everyone brings a gift to someone.
   (c) Everyone respects anyone who has written at least one book.
   (d) Some one person pays all commissions to everyone on the payroll.
   (e) Everyone buys something from all grocers.
   (f) Not everyone wills all his possessions to someone or other.

6. Which of the following are valid, and which invalid?
   (a) $(x)(fx \cdot gx) \cdot \sim(\exists x)fx \cdot \supset \cdot \sim(\exists x)gx.$
   (b) $\sim(\exists x)(fx \cdot gx) \cdot \sim(x)gx \cdot \supset \cdot (\exists x)fx.$
   (c) $(x)(fx \supset gx) \cdot \sim(x)gx \cdot \supset \cdot (x) \sim fx.$
   (d) $\sim(x)(fx \cdot p) \cdot \equiv : (x)fx \cdot \supset \cdot \sim p.$
   (e) $(x)(fx \cdot gx) \cdot \supset : \sim(\exists x)fx \cdot \supset \cdot \sim(\exists x)gx.$
   (f) $(x)(fx \cdot \supset \cdot gx \supset hx) \cdot (\exists x)(gx \cdot \sim hx) \cdot \supset \cdot (\exists x)\sim fx.$
   (g) $(x)(fx \vee gx \cdot \supset \cdot hx) \cdot \sim(\exists x)hx \cdot \supset \cdot (x)\sim(\sim fx \supset gx).$
   (h) $(x)(fx \supset gx) \cdot (x)(fx \supset \sim hx) \cdot (\exists x)fx \cdot \supset \cdot (\exists x)(gx \cdot \sim hx).$
   (i) $(x)(fx \vee gx \cdot \supset \cdot hx \cdot \sim kx) \cdot (\exists x)gx \cdot \supset \cdot (\exists x)\sim kx.$
   (j) $(x)(fx \cdot gx \cdot \supset \cdot hx \vee kx) \cdot (x)(kx \supset \sim fx) \cdot (x)(fx \cdot gx) \cdot \supset \cdot (x)\sim hx.$
   (k) $(\exists x)(y)(\exists z)f(x,y,z) \cdot \supset \cdot (y)\sim(\exists x)(\exists z)f(x,y,z).$
   (l) $(\exists x)(\exists y)(z)f(x,y,z) \cdot \supset \cdot \sim(x)(y)(\exists z)\sim f(x,y,z).$
   (m) $(x)(\exists y)(\exists z)f(x,y,z) \cdot \supset \cdot (\exists y)(x)(\exists z)f(x,y,z).$
   (n) $(\exists x)\sim(y)(z)f(x,y,z) \cdot \supset \cdot (\exists x)(\exists z)(\exists y)\sim f(x,y,z).$
   (o) $(x)(\exists y)(\exists z)f(x,y,z) \cdot \supset \cdot \sim(\exists x)\sim(\exists z)(\exists y)f(x,y,z).$
   (p) $(x)(\exists y)(\exists z)f(x,y,z) \cdot \supset \cdot (x)\sim(z)(y)\sim f(x,y,z).$

[**III**]

Classes

Class Membership and Class Inclusion

The statement

Archimedes is a geometer

is an instance of the formula *"fx"*, in which *"f"* is a predicate variable whose values are properties or attributes, and *"x"* is an individual variable which can be replaced by the proper names of individuals, pronouns, and demonstratives. The statement, thus, can be rephrased in the following way:

Archimedes has the attribute of being a geometer.

The statement has also a further rephrasing, one in which the expression "has the attribute of" gives way to the expression "belongs to the class of":

Archimedes belongs to the class of geometers

or

Archimedes is a member of the class of geometers.

Using the Greek letter *"ε"* to mean "is a member of", and the expression *"ẑ(z is a geometer)"* to mean "the *z*'s such that *z* is a geometer", either of these can be written

Archimedes ε ẑ(z is a geometer).

By putting *"x"* in place of "Archimedes" and *"f"* in place of "geometer' we arrive at the formula

$$x \,\epsilon\, \hat{z}(fz),$$

to the effect that *x* is a member of the things each of which has *f*. This in turn comes to the same thing as saying that *x* is a member of the *class* of things each of which has *f*; and by letting the lower case letters *"a"*, *"b"*, *"c"*, and so on, be class variables, *"x ε ẑ(fz)"* becomes

$$x \,\epsilon\, a.$$

Thus, corresponding to *"fx"*, *"gy"*, etc., in the functional notation we have *"x ε a"*, *"y ε b"*, etc., in the class notation.

60

In similar fashion the statement

All geometers are mathematicians

has two equivalent renderings in English, one in terms of "property" or "attribute", the other in terms of "class" or "set" or "collection":

If anything has the property of being a geometer, it has the property of being a mathematician,

which exemplifies the formula "$(x)(fx \supset gx)$"; and

If anything is a member of the class of geometers, it is a member, or element, of the class of mathematicians,

which exemplifies the formula "$(x)(x \,\epsilon\, a \supset x \,\epsilon\, b)$". When every member of a class a is also a member of a class b, a is said to be *included in* b, the relation of class inclusion being symbolized by "$\subset$". The above formula thus goes into the class formula

$$a \subset b,$$

and the inclusion relation is defined as

$$a \subset b = \text{Df. } (x)(x \,\epsilon\, a \supset x \,\epsilon\, b).$$

Class Products and Sums

A statement about objects which are members of a pair of classes a, b, is said to be about the logical product class,

$$\hat{x}(x \,\epsilon\, a \,.\, x \,\epsilon\, b).$$

This is more compactly written in the form "$a \times b$", or more simply as "ab". The operator symbol "$\times$" for *logical multiplication* is defined as

$$a \times b = \text{Df. } \hat{x}(x \,\epsilon\, a \,.\, x \,\epsilon\, b).^*$$

In the diagram it is represented by the compartment enclosed by the heavy lines. This is the compartment referred to by the formulas "$(\exists x)(x \,\epsilon\, ab)$" and "$\sim(\exists x)(x \,\epsilon\, ab)$", formulas which will be recognized as the counterparts in class notation of the standard I and E statement-forms.

A statement about objects which are members of either of a pair of classes a, b, is said to be about the *logical sum class*,

$$\hat{x}(x \,\epsilon\, a \lor x \,\epsilon\, b),$$

FIGURE 16.

---

* The symbol "$\cap$" is sometimes used instead of "$\times$".

FIGURE 17.

written as "$a + b$". The operator symbol "$+$" for *logical addition* is defined as

$$a + b = \text{Df. } \hat{x}(x \,\epsilon\, a \lor x \,\epsilon\, b).*$$

In the diagram it is represented by the three compartments enclosed by the heavy outer lines. Anything which is a member of the logical sum class of the two classes a, b is a member either of a or of b or of both.

Class Complement

A statement about objects which are not members of a class a is said to be about the *complement* of a and consists of those things which are not members or elements of a,

$$\hat{x} \sim (x \,\epsilon\, a).$$

This is more usually written as "$\bar{a}$".

$$\bar{a} = \text{Df. } \hat{x} \sim (x \,\epsilon\, a).$$

The standard O form of statement can now be rewritten

$$(\exists x)(x \,\epsilon\, a\bar{b}),$$

and the E form may be rewritten

$$a \subset \bar{b}.$$

Class Identity

When we have the conjunction of "$(x)(x \,\epsilon\, a \supset x \,\epsilon\, b)$" with "$(x)(x \,\epsilon\, b \supset x \,\epsilon\, a)$", or alternatively, the equivalence

$$(x)(x \,\epsilon\, a \equiv x \,\epsilon\, b),$$

the classes a, b are said to be one and the same class, or to be *identical*. The symbol for expressing identity between classes is "$=$", and the above formula becomes the more compactly expressed class formula "$a = b$".

$$a = b = \text{Df. } (x)(x \,\epsilon\, a \equiv x \,\epsilon\, b).$$

The Null Class and the Universal Class

In addition to the class variables "a", "b", "c", etc., two special class symbols need to be introduced: the symbol "0" for the *null* class and the symbol "1" for the *universal* class. A usual way of defining the null class

---

* The symbol "$\cup$" is sometimes used instead of "$+$".

is to say that it is the class of those things which are members of both a class a and its complement $\bar{a}$, i.e., which are members of $\hat{x}(x \, \epsilon \, a \, . \, x \, \epsilon \, \bar{a})$, and is expressed as "$a\bar{a}$".

$$0 = \text{Df. } a\bar{a}.$$

Sometimes the symbol "0" is defined by the expression "$\hat{x}(x \neq x)$". Informally, the reasoning which prompts this definition is the following: anything which is a member of the product of a class with its complement will have to be such that it is not identical with itself, as it will be both a member of a and not a member of a. This point is made clear by writing "$\hat{x}(x \, \epsilon \, a \, . \, x \, \epsilon \, \bar{a})$" as "$\hat{x}[x \, \epsilon \, a \, . \sim(x \, \epsilon \, a)]$". Thus the null class may be thought of as a class the members of which are self-contradictory individuals. They will be x's such that $\sim(x = x)$, or, alternatively, $x \neq x$. It is easily seen that the null class has no members:

$$\sim(\exists x)x \, \epsilon \, 0.$$

The universal class 1 can be uniquely described as the complement of the null class,

$$\hat{x}(x = x),$$

and introduced by definition in terms of "0" and "$-$":

$$1 = \text{Df. } \bar{0}.$$

The class equation which can be stated in virtue of this definition, "$1 = \bar{0}$", allows us to arrive at a new class formula,

$$1 = a\bar{a}.$$

This, as will be seen later, yields

$$1 = a + \bar{a}.$$

And just as in the case of the null class, "$\sim(\exists x)x \, \epsilon \, 0$", or "$(x) \sim(x \, \epsilon \, 0)$", holds, so with regard to the universal class the following holds:

$$(x)x \, \epsilon \, 1.$$

This can be seen from the equivalences below.

$$(x)x \, \epsilon \, 1. \equiv . \quad (x)x \, \epsilon \, \bar{0}$$
$$\equiv . \quad (x) \sim(x \, \epsilon \, 0)$$
$$\equiv . \sim(\exists x)x \, \epsilon \, 0.$$

It is of interest to note that the concepts of arithmetic—the notion of integer, or natural number, and the arithmetic operations—are definable by reference to the logical concepts of class and of class addition. Zero is defined as the number of the null class, each succeeding number as a certain kind of class of classes, the rational numbers as ordered pairs of integers, the real numbers as classes of rationals. *Principia Mathematica* is a monument to the thesis that the propositions of pure mathematics are derivable from propositions of logic.

Classes and Categorical Statement-forms

The four standard A, E, I, and O statement-forms expressed in the functional notation can now be reformulated in class terms in a number of different ways. The list below sums them up.

In terms of "ϵ"	In terms of "$=$"	In terms of "$\subset$"
A, $(x)(x \epsilon a \supset x \epsilon b)$ $\sim(\exists x)(x \epsilon a . x \epsilon \bar{b})$	$\bar{a} + b = 1$ $a\bar{b} = 0$	$a \subset b$
E, $(x)(x \epsilon a \supset x \epsilon \bar{b})$ $\sim(\exists x)(x \epsilon a . x \epsilon b)$	$\bar{a} + \bar{b} = 1$ $ab = 0$	$a \subset \bar{b}$
I, $(\exists x)(x \epsilon a . x \epsilon b)$	$ab \neq 0$	$\sim(a \subset \bar{b})$
O, $(\exists x)(x \epsilon a . x \epsilon \bar{b})$	$a\bar{b} \neq 0$	$\sim(a \subset b)$

The case in which being a member of a class a is stated to be both a necessary and sufficient condition for being a member of b has the three representations

$$(x)(x \epsilon a \equiv x \epsilon b), \qquad a = b, \qquad a \subset b . b \subset a.$$

Class Negation, Sums, Products

Recalling that the complement $\bar{a}$ of a given class a is the class of those things which are not members of a, it is intuitively obvious that the *negate* of the complement, $\bar{\bar{a}}$, is the original class a,

$$\bar{\bar{a}} = a.$$

If a is represented by a circle, then what lies outside the circle is the class of those things that are $\bar{a}$, and the class of those things that are $\bar{\bar{a}}$ will lie outside the class $\bar{a}$, and be precisely a.

FIGURE 18.

The complement of ab is $\overline{ab}$, and is identical with the sum class $\bar{a} + \bar{b}$.

$$\overline{ab} = \bar{a} + \bar{b}.$$

The following chain of equations shows this:

$$\begin{aligned} \hat{x}(x \in \overline{ab}) &= \hat{x} \sim(x \in ab) = \hat{x} \sim(x \in a \,.\, x \in b) = \hat{x}[\sim(x \in a) \vee \sim(x \in b)] \\ &= \hat{x}(x \in \bar{a} \vee x \in \bar{b}) = \bar{a} + \bar{b}. \end{aligned}$$

The diagrammatic representation of $\overline{ab}$ will be seen to be also the diagrammatic representation of $\bar{a} + \bar{b}$, the area $\overline{ab}$ outside the heavily outlined compartment ab (including the area outside the circles) being the same as $\bar{a} + \bar{b}$. Any x which falls outside the ab compartment is in $\bar{a}$, $\bar{b}$, or $\bar{a}\bar{b}$, i.e., in the compartment $\bar{a} + \bar{b}$.

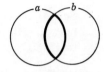

FIGURE 19.

The complement of $a + b$ is $\overline{a + b}$, and is identical with the product class $\bar{a}\bar{b}$:

$$\overline{a + b} = \bar{a}\bar{b}.$$

This is similarly shown by the equation chain of formulas:

$$\begin{aligned} \hat{x}(x \in \overline{a + b}) &= \hat{x} \sim(x \in a + b) = \hat{x} \sim(x \in a \vee x \in b) = \hat{x}[\sim(x \in a) \,.\, \sim(x \in b)] \\ &= \hat{x}(x \in \bar{a} \,.\, x \in \bar{b}) = \bar{a}\bar{b}. \end{aligned}$$

The diagram for $\overline{a + b}$ is also the diagram for the class represented by the area outside that enclosed in heavy lines, i.e., the class which is neither a nor b, or $\bar{a}\bar{b}$. The equations "$\overline{ab} = \bar{a} + \bar{b}$" and "$\overline{a + b} = \bar{a}\bar{b}$" are the so-called De Morgan theorems for the complements of class products and class sums.

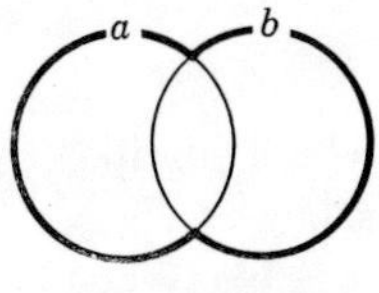

FIGURE 20.

The following list of class equations requires no explanation. The first pair are the *commutative laws* for class multiplication and addition, the second pair the *associative laws* for class multiplication and addition, the third pair the *laws of tautology*:

$$\begin{array}{lll} ab = ba & a(bc) = (ab)c & a \times a = a \\ a + b = b + a & a + (b + c) = (a + b) + c & a + a = a. \end{array}$$

The next five equations are further examples of how class negation operates with respect to "+" and "×".

$$\begin{aligned} &\overline{\bar{a} + \bar{b}} = ab \\ &\overline{\bar{a}\bar{b}} = a + b \\ &\overline{a\bar{a}} = \bar{a} + a = a + \bar{a} \\ &\overline{a + \bar{a}} = \bar{a}a \\ &\overline{(a + b)(cd)} = \overline{a + b} + \overline{cd} = \bar{a}\bar{b} + \bar{c} + \bar{d}. \end{aligned}$$

Distributive Laws

It is important next to see how "+" and "×" operate with respect to each other, when the scope of one falls within the scope of the other. Given the premise

(1) Something is a member of the class of things which are both swift and not winged and is also a member of the class of things which are either carnivorous or both herbivorous and marsupial,

are we entitled to infer the following:

(2) Something is a member of the class of things which are either swift, not winged, and carnivorous, or swift, not winged, herbivorous, and marsupial.

Letting "a" be the class of swift things, "b" the class of things which are winged, "c" the class of carnivores, "d" the class of herbivores, and "e" the class of marsupials, the premise becomes

$$(\exists x)x \; \epsilon \; [a\bar{b}(c + de)],$$

and the conclusion,

$$(\exists x)x \; \epsilon \; (a\bar{b}c + a\bar{b}de).$$

An elementary law of the logic of classes enables us to establish the equation

$$a\bar{b}(c + de) = a\bar{b}c + a\bar{b}de,$$

which justifies the inference of (2) from (1), since expressions equated by a law of classes identify the same class and can replace each other in any formula in which either occurs without changing the truth-value of the formula. The law which is used is one of the two *laws of distribution*, *the rule of distribution with respect to logical multiplication:*

$$a(b + c) = ab + ac.$$

If we diagram these combinations of classes by means of three intersecting circles, it will easily be seen that they are represented by precisely the same part of the diagram. This can perhaps be more easily seen if the formulas are rewritten in the form

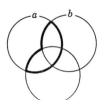

$$\hat{x}(x \; \epsilon \; a \,.\, x \; \epsilon \; b \vee x \; \epsilon \; c) = \hat{x}(x \; \epsilon \; a \,.\, x \; \epsilon \; b \,.\, \vee \,.\, x \; \epsilon \; a \,.\, x \; \epsilon \; c).$$

The remaining law, *the distribution rule with respect to logical addition*, is

FIGURE 21. $$a + bc = (a + b)(a + c).$$

As in the preceding case, the part of the diagram which represents the formula to the left of the identity sign also represents the one on the right. The high-lighted part of the diagram clearly represents $a + bc$. To see that it represents the right-hand product, diagram $a + b$ and $a + c$ separately and combine the diagrams to find their common part. Rewriting the identity in the form

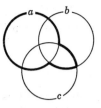

FIGURE 22.

$$\hat{x}(x \in a \,.\, x \in bc) = \hat{x}(x \in a \vee x \in b \,.\, x \in a \vee x \in c)$$

shows that the two sides of the equation are represented by the same set of compartments.

Valid Formulas for 0 and 1

The equations set down so far are laws of logic which cannot fail to yield true class statements, whatever substitutions for the class variables are made. They may be called *valid class formulas*, and the reader has undoubtedly already realized that the class of valid class formulas can be arranged in the form of a deductive system, comparable to the propositional calculus. A class calculus, or algebra of classes, will be constructed later, but for the present we shall continue to consider a number of class formulas informally and, for the most part, without regard to order.

It has already been seen that the null class, if there is one, has no members: $(x) \sim (x \in 0)$. It is not so apparent that there cannot be more than one such class, i.e., that

$$\sim (0_1 \neq 0_2).$$

Let us suppose that there are two distinct null classes, 0_1 and 0_2, such that $0_1 = a\bar{a}$, $0_2 = b\bar{b}$; then

$$a\bar{a} \neq b\bar{b}.$$

This is to suppose that one of these classes has a member that the other lacks, which implies that one of them has a member:

$$(\exists x)(x \in a\bar{a}) \vee (\exists x)(x \in b\bar{b}).$$

Since this is impossible, there can be at most one null class. It follows as a direct consequence that the logical product of any class and its complement is identical with the logical product of any other class and its complement. Thus the class of things that are both men and not men is identical with the class of things that are grasshoppers and also not grasshoppers.

A similar line of reasoning shows that there cannot be more than one universal class:

$$\sim (1_1 \neq 1_2).$$

Again, let us suppose that there are two distinct universal classes, 1_1 and 1_2, and let us identify 1_1 with $a + \bar{a}$, and 1_2 with $b + \bar{b}$:

$$a + \bar{a} \neq b + \bar{b}.$$

By the definition of identity between classes it is clear that on this supposition one of these two classes must lack an element which the other has,

$$(\exists x) \sim(x \,\epsilon\, a + \bar{a}) \vee (\exists x) \sim(x \,\epsilon\, b + \bar{b}),$$

and thus that the null class has a member: $(\exists x)(x \,\epsilon\, a\bar{a}) \vee (\exists x)(x \,\epsilon\, b\bar{b})$. Hence, $\sim(1_1 \neq 1_2)$. An immediate consequence of this is that the logical sum of any class and its complement is identical with the logical sum of any other class and its complement.

It should be pointed out that a special kind of restriction has to be imposed on the universal class: it must be confined to what may be called a logical universe of discourse. The formula "$(x)x \,\epsilon\, 1$" is valid only so long as the range of "x" is limited to objects of the same *logical type*, which in the present case are individuals. The Theory of Logical Types cannot be gone into here; but to give a glimpse of its nature, were 1 not confined to objects of one logical kind, for example, were it allowed to have as members any class c and the elements of c as well, then 1 would become an illegitimate totality. That is, if e is a member of c then "$e \,\epsilon\, 1$" and "$c \,\epsilon\, 1$" are not both instances of "$x \,\epsilon\, 1$". The range of "x" in "$x \,\epsilon\, 1$" is all individuals, not all possible objects.

Several formulas concerning the classes 0 and 1 are in order at this point:

$$a0 = 0$$
$$a + 0 = a$$
$$a1 = a$$
$$a + 1 = 1.$$

No more than a cursory examination of the first two formulas is necessary in order to be convinced that they are valid class formulas. The negation of the first equation, "$\sim(a0 = 0)$", to the effect that one of the two classes has a member which the other lacks, has the consequence

$$(\exists x)(x \,\epsilon\, a \,.\, x \,\epsilon\, 0) \vee (\exists x)(x \,\epsilon\, 0),$$

which in turn has the consequence

$$(\exists x)x \,\epsilon\, 0.$$

The negation of the second, "$\sim(a + 0 = a)$", has the consequence

$$\sim(x)(x \,\epsilon\, a + 0 \,.\, \supset \,.\, x \,\epsilon\, a),$$

which implies

$$(\exists x)x \,\epsilon\, a \vee x \,\epsilon\, 0 \,.\, \sim(x \,\epsilon\, a).$$

Something which is a member either of a or of 0 and is not a member of a must be a member of 0; and again we have the illegitimate consequence that $(\exists x)x \,\epsilon\, 0$.

A diagram will be sufficient to show that the second pair of equations, "$a1 = a$" and "$a + 1 = 1$", are valid formulas. Let us represent 1 by a square, and any class a included in and distinct from 1 by a circle inside the square. The diagram shows the class $a1$ to be identical with a, and the class $a + 1$ to be identical with 1. The common part of a and 1, their *intersection*, is a; and since no segment of a extends beyond 1, their logical sum is 1. In the trivial case where a is itself 1, the two equations obviously hold.

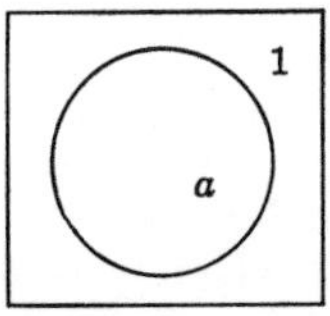

FIGURE 23.

Laws of Absorption

The next three formulas, called *absorption* formulas, can also be seen to be valid class formulas from their diagrammatic representations:

$$a + ab = a$$
$$a(a + b) = a$$
$$ab + a\bar{b} = a.$$

All are represented by the same part of the diagram.

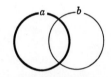

FIGURE 24.

Reduction Problems

It will be of some interest at this point, before the algebra of classes is erected, to do some elementary, informally conducted computing with classes. In accordance with the commutative laws (p. 65) we shall change the order of the terms in sums and products in any way we please; and as permitted by the associative laws (p. 65) we shall also rebracket sums and products (but not combinations of sums and products) in any way useful to the solution of a problem. Thus "$a + bc + d$" may be changed to "$a + d + cb$", and it may be bracketed as "$(a + bc) + d$" or as "$a + (bc + d)$", but not as "$(a + b)(c + d)$".

Let the problem be to determine whether

the class of people who are both blonde and tall or else blonde and not tall, and also either broad-shouldered or else broad-shouldered and loose-jointed

is identical with

the class of people who are blonde and broad-shouldered.

Let "a" be the class of blonde people, "b" the class of tall people, "c" the class of broad-shouldered people, "d" the class of loose-jointed people. The problem is to discover whether

$$(ab + a\bar{b})(c + cd) = ac$$

is a valid class formula. The two sums on the left of "=" contract, respectively, into "a" and "c" by the third and first of the above laws of absorption, so that we have the identity

$$ac = ac.$$

The left-hand expression thus transforms into the one on the right, and the classes denoted are identical.

In the next problems computations will be made without comment or reference back to valid formulas. Justification is left to the reader. Given the equation below, to show that it is valid by the process of *reduction to an identity*:

$$
\begin{aligned}
a(b + \bar{c}) + a\bar{c} + bd + bc + b\bar{d} + ac \quad &= a + b\\
(ab + a\bar{c}) + a\bar{c} + bd + bc + b\bar{d} + ac \quad &=\\
ab + (a\bar{c} + a\bar{c}) + (bd + b\bar{d}) + bc + ac &=\\
ab + a\bar{c} + b + bc + ac \quad &=\\
(b + ba) + (a\bar{c} + ac) + (b + bc) \quad &=\\
b + a + b \quad &=\\
a + (b + b) \quad &=\\
a + b \quad &= a + b
\end{aligned}
$$

Problem: to reduce to an identity

$$
\begin{aligned}
ab\bar{c} + bc + \bar{a} + cd + \bar{b} + c + de \quad &= 1\\
ab\bar{c} + (\bar{a} + \bar{b} + c) + (bc + cd + de) &=\\
(ab\bar{c} + \overline{ab\bar{c}}) + (bc + cd + de) \quad &=\\
1 + (bc + cd + de) \quad &=\\
1 \quad &= 1
\end{aligned}
$$

Problem: to reduce to an identity

$$
\begin{aligned}
a(\bar{a}b + \bar{a}\bar{b} + \bar{a}\bar{d}) &= 0\\
a(\bar{a} + \bar{a}\bar{d}) \quad &=\\
a\bar{a} \quad &=\\
0 \quad &= 0
\end{aligned}
$$

The Antilogism

We hark back briefly to syllogistic reasoning in order to acquaint the reader with a simplification in the test of syllogisms effected by means of the equation and inequation class notation. A syllogism is valid if its conclusion *follows* from the premises; and the conclusion follows from the premises only if the negation of the conclusion is inconsistent with the premises. Thus a syllogism is valid only if negating its conclusion results in an inconsistent conjunction of statements. For example, on negating the conclusion of the syllogism

> All teachers are slave drivers
> All slave drivers are slothful
> ―――――――――――――――――
> All teachers are slothful

the result is the conjunction of the first two statements with "Some teachers are not slothful", a patently inconsistent conjunction. But negating the conclusion of the invalid syllogism

> All slave drivers are cruel
> All teachers are cruel
> ―――――――――――――――――
> Some slave drivers are teachers

gives the conjunction of the premises with "No slave drivers are teachers", a triad of statements which is not inconsistent. A simple diagrammatic method of evaluating syllogisms suggests itself immediately. Instead of diagramming the syllogism we diagram the triad of statements obtained by negating the conclusion of the syllogism, and if the diagram has a "contradictory" compartment, i.e., a compartment which is both shaded and has a cross, the syllogism is valid, otherwise it is not valid. Letting a = teachers, b = slave drivers, c = slothful people, d = cruel people, the two diagrams are

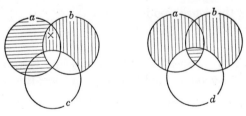

FIGURE 25.

The cross is made to span two compartments in order to indicate that one or the other is membered.

This method is sufficient for testing any syllogism, but it is instructive to see what the conditions are to which a triad of equations and inequations must conform in order to be an inconsistent set, or to be an *antilogism*. It is easily seen that every valid syllogism is equivalent to a syllogism composed of three universals. That this is the case is guaranteed by the syllogistic rules (3) and (4) (p. 43) and the equivalence

$$p \cdot q \cdot \supset \cdot r : \equiv : p \cdot \sim r \cdot \supset \cdot \sim q : \equiv : q \cdot \sim r \cdot \supset \cdot \sim p.$$

Hence it is necessary only to discover the logical properties which all valid syllogisms of three universals have in common in order to formulate the necessary and sufficient conditions for syllogistic validity. Negating the conclusion of such a syllogism we obtain a triad composed of two universals and one particular, or two equations and one inequation, and only valid syllogisms correspond to such a triad. In order, therefore, for a triad of equations and inequations to form an inconsistent set, (1) it must be composed of two equations and one inequation. This, however, is not sufficient. There are two further conditions, (2) the common term of the equations must occur as complements of each other, and (3) the terms of the inequation must occur exactly as they appear in the equations. Conditions (1) through (3) are both necessary and sufficient for a triad's being an antilogism, i.e., for a triad's being such that any two of the statements will imply the negative of the remaining one. The antilogistic procedure for testing a syllogism is to negate the given conclusion and see whether the resulting set answers to conditions (1) through (3). If it does, the set is an antilogism and the original syllogism is valid; otherwise the syllogism is invalid. Two syllogisms, one valid and one invalid, are tested below by this method.

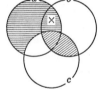

(1) Some Franciscans are meditative	$ab \neq 0$
No buccaneers are meditative	$cb = 0$
Some Franciscans are not buccaneers	$a\bar{c} \neq 0$

The negation of the conclusion is $\quad a\bar{c} = 0.$

FIGURE 26.

The triad obtained satisfies (1) through (3) and is an antilogism. The syllogism is valid, therefore, and the diagram bears this out.

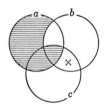

(2) All cassowaries are ungainly	$a\bar{b} = 0$
No prehistoric creature is a cassowary	$ca = 0$
No prehistoric creature is ungainly	$cb = 0$

The negation of the conclusion is $\quad cb \neq 0.$

FIGURE 27.

The triad obtained violates conditions (2) and (3) and is not an antilogism. The syllogism is invalid and the diagram bears this out.

The Algebra of Classes

We proceed to the construction of the deductive system of class formulas. It will be seen that some of the valid class formulas stated in the preceding sections are used as axioms of the system while others enter into the system as theorems. The axioms for the algebra, or calculus, of classes presented here are formulated in terms of the operator symbols "$\times$" and "$-$", the relation symbol "$=$", and the class variables "a", "b", "c", ... A number of conditions are imposed on the set K of classes which enter into the algebra. These conditions are usually counted as axioms of the algebra; but it seems preferable to think of them as presuppositions of the algebraic system, instead of axioms, particularly since theorems are not derived from them by the usual procedure of substituting on variables. They are

  K1 If $a \,\epsilon\, K$ and $b \,\epsilon\, K$, then $a \times b \,\epsilon\, K$
  K2 If $a \,\epsilon\, K$, then $\bar{a} \,\epsilon\, K$
  K3 There are at least two distinct classes in K.

The algebra of classes rests on the logic of equality, comprised of the functional calculus of first order with added axioms for identity. Principles for deducing theorems in that calculus, among them the transformation rules of the propositional calculus which it contains as a part, automatically become rules of deduction in the algebra of classes. The properties of the relation of equality, or identity, which are developed in the logic of equality are presupposed by the algebra of classes. The following give three basic properties, and are in fact the axioms for one formulation of the logic of equality.

  E1 $x = x$
  E2 $x = y \,.\, \supset \,.\, y = x$
  E3 $x = y \,.\, y = z \,.\, \supset \,.\, x = z.$

An examination of these will reassure the reader that he does not need to possess detailed knowledge of the logic of equality in order to be able to work with the algebra of classes.

With K1 through K3 and E1 through E3 presupposed, the axioms are three in number:

  (1) $a \times b = b \times a$
  (2) $\overline{(a \times b)} \times c = a \times \overline{(b \times c)}$
  (3) $\overline{(\bar{a} \times \bar{b})} \times \overline{(\bar{a} \times b)} = a$

These are an adaptation of postulates formulated by E. V. Huntington.[*] Note that no postulates for 0 and 1 are included. The symbols "0" and

---

[*] "Boolean Algebra. A Correction," *Trans. Am. Math. Soc.*, vol. 35, p. 557, 1933.

"1" are definitionally introduced, and definitions are also given of "$a + b$" and of "$a \subset b$".

$$
\begin{aligned}
\text{(A)} \quad & a + b = \text{Df. } \overline{\bar{a} \times \bar{b}} \\
\text{(B)} \quad & 0 = \text{Df. } a \times \bar{a} \\
\text{(C)} \quad & 1 = \text{Df. } \overline{a \times \bar{a}} \\
\text{(D)} \quad & a \subset b = \text{Df. } ab = a
\end{aligned}
$$

The rules for deducing class theorems are the following:

R1   From A the result of substituting class expressions for each occurrence of the same class variable in A may be inferred

R2   From A the result of replacing class expressions by their equivalents may be inferred.

Rule R1 operates under the condition of completeness, that is to say, the same substitution must be made for all occurrences of a given variable in A.   Rule R2 dispenses with this condition.   The next two rules are modus ponens and the rule of inference called the Deduction Theorem.

R3   From A and A $\supset$ B, B may be inferred

R4   If from $A_1, A_2, \ldots, A_n$ taken as hypotheses B is deducible, then $A_1, A_2, \ldots, A_{n-1}, A_n \supset B$ may be inferred.

The axioms are stated again for convenient reference and we proceed to proofs of theorems.   To make the first three proofs easier to read superscripts are used to indicate the number of bars over a variable.

(1) $a \times b = b \times a$

(2) $(a \times b) \times c = a \times (b \times c)$

(3) $\overline{\bar{a} \times \bar{b}} \times \overline{\bar{a} \times b} = a$

(4) $a \times \bar{a} = \bar{a} \times \bar{\bar{a}}$

(3), $\bar{a}$ for b]	$\overline{a^1 \times a^3} \times \overline{a^1 \times a^2} = a$	i
(3), $\bar{\bar{a}}$ for b, $\bar{a}$ for a]	$\overline{a^2 \times a^3} \times \overline{a^2 \times a^2} = \bar{a}$	ii
(1), i, ii, R2]	$a \times \bar{a} = [\overline{a^1 \times a^3} \times \overline{a^1 \times a^2}]$	
	$\times [\overline{a^2 \times a^3} \times \overline{a^2 \times a^2}]$	iii
(3), $\bar{a}$ for a, $\bar{a}$ for b]	$\overline{a^3 \times a^2} \times \overline{a^3 \times a^1} = \bar{\bar{a}}$	iv
(3), $\bar{a}$ for a, $\bar{a}$ for b]	$\overline{a^2 \times a^2} \times \overline{a^2 \times a^1} = \bar{a}$	v
(1), iv, v, R2]	$\bar{a} \times \bar{\bar{a}} = [\overline{a^2 \times a^2} \times \overline{a^2 \times a^1}]$	
	$\times [\overline{a^3 \times a^2} \times \overline{a^3 \times a^1}]$	vi
(1), (2), iii, vi, R2]	$a \times \bar{a} = \bar{a} \times \bar{\bar{a}}$	

(5) $\bar{\bar{a}} = a$

    (3), $\bar{a}$ for a, a for b] $\overline{a^3 \times a^2} \times \overline{a^3 \times a^1} = \bar{\bar{a}}$ i

    (3), $\bar{a}$ for b] $\overline{a^1 \times a^3} \times \overline{a^1 \times a^2} = a$ ii

    (4), $\bar{a}$ for a] $a^1 \times a^2 = a^2 \times a^3$ iii

    (1), i, ii, iii, R2] $a = \bar{\bar{a}}$

(6) $a \times \bar{a} = b \times \bar{b}$

    (3), $\bar{b}$ for b] $\overline{a^1 \times b^2} \times \overline{a^1 \times b^1} = a$ i

    (3), $\bar{a}$ for a, $\bar{b}$ for b] $\overline{a^2 \times b^2} \times \overline{a^2 \times b^1} = \bar{a}$ ii

    (1), i, ii, R2] $a \times \bar{a} = [\overline{a^1 \times b^2} \times \overline{a^1 \times b^1}]$

                           $\times [\overline{a^2 \times b^2} \times \overline{a^2 \times b^1}]$ iii

    (3), b for a, a for b] $\overline{b^1 \times a^1} \times \overline{b^1 \times a} = b$ iv

    iv, $\bar{a}$ for a] $\overline{b^1 \times a^2} \times \overline{b^1 \times a^1} = b$ v

    iv, $\bar{b}$ for b, $\bar{a}$ for a] $\overline{b^2 \times a^2} \times \overline{b^2 \times a^1} = \bar{b}$ vi

    (1), v, vi, R2] $[\overline{b^1 \times a^2} \times \overline{b^1 \times a^1}]$

                        $\times [\overline{b^2 \times a^2} \times \overline{b^2 \times a^1}] = b \times \bar{b}$ vii

    (1), (2), iii, vii, R2] $a \times \bar{a} = b \times \bar{b}$

(7) $0 = \bar{a} \times a$

    (1), $\bar{a}$ for b, Df.B] $0 = \bar{a} \times a$

Conditions K1 and K2 assure the existence of a special element, $\bar{a}a$, in K. Theorem (7) identifies this element as 0, which by (6) is shown to be unique.

(8) $0 = \bar{1}$

    (5), $a \times \bar{a}$ for a] $a \times \bar{a} = \overline{\overline{a \times \bar{a}}}$ i

    i, Df.B] $0 = \overline{\overline{a \times \bar{a}}}$ ii

    ii, Df.C] $0 = \bar{1}$

(9) $1 = \bar{0}$

    (5), 0 for a] $0^3 = \bar{0}$ i

    i, (8)] $1^4 = \bar{0}$ ii

    ii, (5)] $1^2 = \bar{0}$ iii

    iii, (5)] $1 = \bar{0}$

(10) $a + \bar{a} = 1$

    (9), Df.C] $\bar{0} = \overline{a \times \bar{a}}$ i

    (4), (1), i] $\bar{0} = \overline{a \times \bar{\bar{a}}}$ ii

    ii, Df.A, (9)] $1 = a + \bar{a}$

Theorems (11) through (19) are given without proof, some of them for their intrinsic interest and some for their usefulness in proving further theorems.

(11) $a \times 1 = a$, $a \subset 1$ (By Df.D)

(12) $a \times a = a$, $a \subset a$ (By Df.D)

(13) $a + 0 = a$

(14) $a + b = b + a$

(15) $a + a = a$

(16) $a \times 0 = 0$, $0 \subset a$

(17) $a + 1 = 1$

(18) $a + ab = a$

(19) $a(a + b) = a$, $a \subset a + b$

(20) $ab \subset a$

   (2), a for b, b for c] $(a \times a)b = a \times (a \times b)$ i
   (2), a for c] $(a \times b)a = a \times (b \times a)$ ii
   (1)] $(a \times b)a = a \times (a \times b)$ iii
   (12)] $(a \times a) \times b = a \times b$ iv
   R2, i, iii, iv] $a \times b = a \times (a \times b)$ v
   (1), v, Df.D $ab \subset a$

(21) $a + (b \times c) = (a + b) \times (a + c)$

(22) $a \times (b + c) = (a \times b) + (a \times c)$

(23) $a = ab + a\bar{b}$

   (11), $b + \bar{b}$ for 1, by (10)] $a = a \times (b + \bar{b})$
   i, (22), b for c] $a = ab + a\bar{b}$

(24) $(a + \bar{b}) \times (a + b) = a$

   (3), $\bar{b}$ for b] $\overline{(\bar{a} \times \bar{\bar{b}}) \times (\bar{a} \times \bar{b})} = a$ i
   i, Df.A] $(a + \bar{b}) \times (a + b) = a$

The following illustrate the use of R4. An antecedent used as a hypothesis is indicated by "Hyp".

(25) $a = b . \supset . ac = bc$

   (1), b for a, c for b] $bc = cb$ i
   Hyp] $ac = cb$ ii
   R4, ii, (1)] $a = b . \supset . ac = bc$

When a substitution of one expression for another is made because an equivalence between them is *assumed*, the result B is not a theorem about classes but something true only *hypothetically*. But provided B can be deduced from valid formulas in which substitution has been made in accordance with assumption A, R4 allows A $\supset$ B to be asserted as a theorem.

(26) $b = \bar{a} \,.\, \supset \,.\, a = \bar{b}$

    (22), Hyp] $a = a\bar{a} + a\bar{b}$

    (7), (1)] $= 0 + a\bar{b}$

    (13), (14)] $a = a\bar{b}$ i

    (23), b for a, a for b] $\bar{b} = \bar{b}a + \bar{b}\bar{a}$

    Hyp] $= \bar{b}a + \bar{b}b$

    (7)] $= \bar{b}a + 0$

    (13), $\bar{b}a$ for a] $= \bar{b}a$

    (1)] $\bar{b} = a\bar{b}$ ii

    i, ii, R2] $a = \bar{b}$

    R4] $b = \bar{a} \,.\, \supset \,.\, a = \bar{b}$

(27) $a \subset b \,.\, b \subset a \,.\, \supset \,.\, a = b$

    Hyp, by Df.D] $a \times b = a \,.\, b \times a = b$

    (1)] $a \times b = a \,.\, a \times b = b$

    R2] $a = b$

    R4] $a \subset b \,.\, b \subset a \,.\, \supset \,.\, a = b$

The next proof illustrates the use of R3.

(28) $\bar{a} \subset a \,.\, \supset \,.\, a = 1$

    Hyp, Df.D] $\bar{a} \times a = \bar{a}$ i

    (7)] $0 = \bar{a}$ ii

    (26), 0 for b] $0 = \bar{a} \,.\, \supset \,.\, a = \bar{0}$ iii

    ii, iii, R3] $a = \bar{0}$ iv

    iv, (8)] $a = 1$ v

    v, R4] $\bar{a} \subset a \,.\, \supset \,.\, a = 1$

EXERCISES

1. Rewrite the following statements with the help of "$=$" and "0", "$=$" and "1", "ϵ" and "$\supset$", and "$\subset$", "$^{-}$", and "$\sim$":

        No philanthropists are chauvinists

        All patriots are single-minded

        Some pessimists are not hypochondriacs

        Only odd numbers greater than 2 are prime

        All and only elephants have trunks

        There is a real root of $x^2 = 4$.

2. Show informally that the following formulas are valid, and check by diagrams whenever possible.

    (1) $a \subset a + \bar{b} + c$

    (2) $\bar{a}b \subset b$

    (3) $\overline{\bar{a} + b\bar{c}} = a(\bar{b} + c)$

    (4) $\bar{a}\bar{b}c \subset \bar{b}$

    (5) $\bar{b} \subset \overline{\bar{a}b}$, $\bar{a}b \subset \bar{b}$

    (6) $a \subset \overline{\bar{a}b}$

(7) $a \subset 1$

(8) $0 \subset a$

(9) $a\bar{b}(bc + d) = a\bar{b}d$

(10) $\bar{a} + bcd = (\bar{a} + b)(\bar{a} + c)(\bar{a} + d)$

(11) $a + bc + de + \bar{c} + \overline{(a + b)(a + c)} = 1$

(12) $\overline{a(b + c)} + c + \bar{d} + \overline{ef} + ab + e\bar{c} + ac = 1$

(13) $\overline{ab\bar{a}c} + \bar{c} + de + a(b + c) = 1$

(14) $a(b + c + \bar{d}) + b\bar{d} + abcd + a\bar{b} + d = a + b + d$

(15) $\overline{\overline{ab} + \overline{cd}} + \overline{\overline{ab} + dc} + a = a$

3. Apply the antilogistic test to the following and confirm by diagrams.

   (a) All professors are nearsighted. All nearsighted people are timid. Hence all professors are timid.

   (b) No vegetarians are boisterous. No refined people are boisterous. Therefore no refined people are vegetarians.

   (c) No ballerina is a clown. Some clowns are not agile. Hence some ballerinas are agile.

   (d) All gazelles are graceful. Some graceful creatures are swift. Hence some gazelles are swift.

   (e) All college students adore logic and all who adore logic are not fickle. Hence no college student is fickle.

   (f) Some camels are not longlived. All dromedaries are camels. Hence some animals that are not longlived are dromedaries.

   (g) No buttercup has an odor. Some buttercups are Easter-egg yellow. Hence some things which have an odor are not Easter-egg yellow.

   (h) All horticulturists love dirt. Some lovers of dirt are not generous. Hence some horticulturists are generous.

   (i) All taxidermists are pessimists. All pessimists hate animals. Hence some taxidermists hate animals.

4. (a) Prove (5), $\bar{\bar{a}} = a$, using (26) and (11). HINT: put $\bar{a} \times 1$ for b in (26).

   (b) Prove (18), $a + ab = a$, using (22), (17), (11). HINT: put 1 for b, b for c in (22).

   (c) Prove (19), $a \times (a + b) = a$. HINT: Use (18), (15).

   (d) Prove $a \subset c . \supset . ab \subset ac$. Use (2).

   (e) Prove $a \subset b . c \subset d . \supset . ac \subset bd$. Use (1), (2).

   (f) Prove $a\bar{b} = 0 . \supset . ab = a$. Use (23).

   (g) Prove $ab = a . \supset . a\bar{b} = 0$. Use (25), (2).

   (h) Prove $1 = (a + \bar{a})(b + \bar{b})$. Use (10), (23).

   (i) Prove $(a + b)(c + d) = (ac + bc) + (ad + bd)$. Use (22), (21).

   (j) Prove $a = a + ab + ac + ad$. Use (18).

   (k) $ab = 0 . a \neq 0 . \supset . a\bar{b} \neq 0$. Use (23).